CW01083012

I sometimes received begging or threatening letters asking to bypass the waiting list. One was from a Labour Member of Parliament who … asked, on House of Commons notepaper, for his daughter's operation to be brought forward because of repeated illness and missed schooldays, and enclosed a letter from her teacher. I showed it to a fellow Senior Registrar as we rummaged around our respective waiting lists.

"Bring her in!" he said. "Always bow to authority and influence. She is only a little girl who needs surgery, not the frontline of your battle for fairness!"

That colleague also ended up with a knighthood and the presidency of one of our Royal Colleges.

*

When I saw the dictator for his final consultation he asked if his headaches would cease. I pointed out that headaches can have many causes and suggested that a man in his position must often be under stress. He looked at me coldly and said he also had the sensation that plotters were around him and wondered if that was normal.

The interpreter looked as though he was having a heart attack; his skin was grey with sweat around the lips when I asked if it was possible that they were really scheming.

"We plotted against my predecessor," he said flatly, "and we killed him."

*

At the memorial service his family introduced me to one of his very old and very deaf relatives.

"It's the doctor," they explained. "He looked after him."

The old man shouted back as deaf people do.

"He could not have been much good if he died!"

Everyone said "shush" and whispered that it was not my fault.

TO HEAR AGAIN, TO SING AGAIN

A Memoir by Ellis Douek,
ENT Surgeon and Hearing Implant Pioneer

Other Titles by the Author

The Sense of Smell and Its Abnormalities
A Middle Eastern Affair

Other World Scientific Titles by the Author

Overcoming Deafness: The Story of Hearing and Language
ISBN: 978-1-78326-464-3
ISBN: 978-1-78326-465-0 (pbk)

TO HEAR AGAIN, TO SING AGAIN

A Memoir by Ellis Douek, ENT Surgeon and Hearing Implant Pioneer

ELLIS DOUEK

Guy's and St Thomas' Hospital, UK

NEW JERSEY • LONDON • SINGAPORE • BEIJING • SHANGHAI • HONG KONG • TAIPEI • CHENNAI • TOKYO

Published by

World Scientific Publishing Co. Pte. Ltd.
5 Toh Tuck Link, Singapore 596224
USA office: 27 Warren Street, Suite 401-402, Hackensack, NJ 07601
UK office: 57 Shelton Street, Covent Garden, London WC2H 9HE

Library of Congress Cataloging-in-Publication Data
Names: Douek, Ellis, 1934– author.
Title: To hear again, to sing again : a memoir by Ellis Douek, ENT surgeon and hearing implant pioneer / Ellis Douek.
Description: New Jersey : World Scientific, [2022] | Includes index.
Identifiers: LCCN 2022003343 | ISBN 9789811255434 (hardcover) | ISBN 9789811255441 (ebook for institutions) | ISBN 9789811255458 (ebook for individuals)
Subjects: LCSH: Douek, Ellis, 1934– | Otolaryngologists--Great Britain--Biography. | Surgeons--Great Britain--Biography. | Otolaryngology, Operative--Great Britain--History. | Cochlear implants--Great Britain--History.
Classification: LCC RF38.D68 A3 2022 | DDC 617.5/10092 [B]--dc23/eng/20220613
LC record available at https://lccn.loc.gov/2022003343

British Library Cataloguing-in-Publication Data
A catalogue record for this book is available from the British Library.

For any available supplementary material, please visit
https://www.worldscientific.com/worldscibooks/10.1142/12811#t=suppl

Desk Editor: Shaun Tan Yi Jie

Typeset by Stallion Press
Email: enquiries@stallionpress.com

To Danny and Joel who grew up with it
and to Leo and all the new doctors who face such an exciting world

Preface

Surgeons' lives in the first half of the 20th century were coloured by war. Their concerns had been wound management and exposure to horrifying weapons, from poison gas at the start of that woeful epoch to atomic radiation in the end.

The second half of that century, my half, has been fortunate as, in a time of relative peace, antibiotics not only cured most bacterial infections including tuberculosis and syphilis but also allowed extraordinary new surgical interventions. The operating microscope completely changed what my own specialty could do and the surgery of deafness evolved dramatically. During our half century we found the means to do at least something for every type of deafness. Today most of our residual hearing problems are the result of aging and that is what we must deal with. What we want is not just to hear but to hear well however old we get, even to hear perfectly. It means that although we have accomplished a lot we still have much to do.

We were told, as medical students in 1951, that our life expectancy was 66 years and the life span allocated to us seemed adequate. Now, well past that deadline, it is possible to look back with satisfaction not just because we have, as a generation, already outlived our destiny by a couple of decades but because our achievements, including that of making deaf people hear, have been well beyond any expectations we may have had.

Before our time there was little that medicine or surgery could do for people other than relieve pain and make them comfortable until the advent of antibiotics. Heroic surgery often failed as a result of infection and some of the procedures offered by surgeons were misguided to say the least, and yet our predecessors thrived as a profession as they had a role in society which is not entirely the one we have now. They were somebody to turn to and the good doctor developed trust and inspired confidence even though there was little that he could offer while the surgeon, called in for amputations or draining abscesses, was not even granted the title of "doctor".

Ours has been a pivotal time in which to be a surgeon and I have enjoyed working in many of the finest centres. My colleagues showed remarkable skills and talents and it has been a rare pleasure to spend my life in the company of people I held in such high regard.

I took part in developments which have helped make deafness more manageable, but another element has been even more important in my life and that is getting to know patients by caring for them.

When I interviewed young candidates for admission to our Medical School at Guy's they all expressed the wish, perhaps the need, to help people. I then had to judge their aptitude and capacity to do this as a doctor rather than as something else equally praiseworthy, but at the heart of it all there remained the wish to be of help to those in pain and distress.

Looking back at my life has been like examining a colourful tapestry but it does not seem continuous, one thing inevitably leading to another. It appears to me like a series of distinct events which have taken me by surprise. Interesting and often extraordinary observations revealed how all sorts of people live and behave. Doctors have always juxtaposed the rich with the poor, the powerless and vulnerable with Emperors and Kings, and medicine has traditionally allowed the son of a nobody to place his hand on the tyrant's abdomen.

There was no air travel in the first half of the 20th century whereas I was able to visit hospitals all over the world. Emerging in the car park of the Hospital Cantonal in Geneva I remember my assistant saying, "Wait a moment! Have you noticed?" What he was pointing out was: "Their car park is cleaner than our hospital!" He was exaggerating but I learned a thing or two and I taught also. I was a visiting Professor at Johns Hopkins in Baltimore and I taught at the Free University in Amsterdam. I gave a course in Beijing and went to the Persian Gulf. Everywhere I may have learned more than I taught.

The way my life has turned out has been happy and absorbing as lives go, though likely to interest only a few. On the other hand I look back to my time as a surgeon with wonder, as what I have experienced or observed seems like a succession of exciting and often perplexing episodes.

Contents

Looking Back

Perhaps our lives will not have been fully lived until we look back.

We had a minor celebration at the *Miller of Mansfield*, the pub behind Guy's Hospital where I was a consultant Ear, Nose and Throat (ENT) surgeon, though it could not have been important as the *Miller* is rather soulless, unlike the *George* with its ancient gallery, or the *Anchor* on the river which we used for grander occasions.

"The last time I was here," the older of my colleagues, Leslie Salmon, had said, "someone I do not remember ever having seen before asked if I was the Ear, Nose and Throat surgeon."

The man had gone on to say that 20 years before Mr Salmon had given him six months to live so, unsure how to reply, he had felt obliged to congratulate him on looking so well.

"I am quite certain," he had added, "that I have never *given* anyone six months to live, as though it were a sentence. We don't do that sort of thing do we?"

Memories alter, and even those shared are rarely identical.

*

There are also two histories, the one which chronicles the major events of our time and that which we have witnessed ourselves, the little history of 'mice and men'.

Had I failed to get into medical school I might well have had to fight in the Korean War which did not end until 1953.

Luckily however, I was a student at King's College London during that war, when more than 1,000 British soldiers were killed and almost 3,000 wounded. There were over 36,000 Americans dead as well as countless Koreans and Chinese. British and Australian troops also fought in the Malayan Emergency, a guerrilla war in what later became Malaysia, a war where 500 of our soldiers died and thousands were wounded. The Cyprus Insurgency began in 1954, and two years later the Suez War, but I was still a clinical student at Westminster Hospital.

I do not know why some of those actions were called wars while others were 'emergencies' or 'insurgencies' but I did not have to take part in any of them, and I was only conscripted when they were over serving in Scotland as the doctor of the Black Watch and of the Argyll and Sutherland Highlanders.

I still occasionally wear a tartan tie and very often someone informs me that I should not be wearing it as it is reserved for the Black Watch. Of course, it amuses me to say that I had indeed served with that brave regiment and watch the disbelief on their face, but I realise it is silly to care and I wonder why it is assumed that I could not have been a Black Watch officer.

Much of that time is now forgotten and fortunately, I had not been put in the position to kill or be killed but I also feel that it was right for me, born in the first half of the 20th century, to have been in the army. Virtually everyone of my age or older, in most countries, has done military service so I have been a man of my time. Compulsory military service ended in the United Kingdom in 1962 when Macmillan was Prime Minister and I returned to London to work as a House Surgeon, the most junior position in our Health Service.

*

At the start of my life as a doctor, events governing surgery were held at the Royal Society of Medicine in Wimpole Street and, young and anxious to make our mark, we tried to present our work in the morning, as havoc reigned in the afternoon after the projectionist had got drunk over lunch.

On one occasion the invited speaker, a Belgian who had some difficulty with English, was in tears as his slides came upside down and at random. The projectionist, unshaven and ill-tempered, tottered while mumbling obscenities and went on to drop the slides on the floor, sending us junior doctors fumbling in the dark on all fours to retrieve as many as we could while someone poured the lecturer a glass of water.

Today's visual aids, stored in an electromagnetic cloud, may go on being called 'slides' although they are no longer objects, and perhaps that term, suggestive of something fleeting, will linger as dictionaries discuss how it came to mean an image. When I started my studies the slide shows that were to become a familiar teaching tool had just been introduced and we drew in chalk on the blackboard.

Aging surgeons then placed themselves at the front because they had problems hearing, not in order to assert themselves, but we mocked and mouthed their words when one of them raised his hand as they were always the same.

"I remember a case!" they invariably began.

What inspired us were the statistics and percentages of a science where reminiscences were beginning to have no place.

The vascular surgeon at our hospital, tired perhaps of stripping varicose veins, had turned to the heart and attempted to improve blood flow by widening valves scarred by disease. He did this by scratching at them with a fingernail grown especially long and as there were no bypass machines we watched him operate on the beating organ. In the absence of defibrillators, if it stopped the patient died.

Results were poor but some survived so here we are.

*

Chemists concealed the names of the drugs they dispensed, covering the bottle with labels that said "THE MEDICINE", as patients were not supposed to know what they took. It must have seemed the right thing to do at the time.

People shouted at the deaf and sometimes mocked them as political correctness had not been invented. The Medical Research Council had devised a hearing aid the size of a packet of cigarettes where a wire led to an earpiece that often whistled and made noises when rubbed, but it was a big advance as earlier batteries had been the size of a car. The Post

Office, ordered to make and market it by a government ideologically committed to end private venture, had done an adequate job but it also killed off all independent manufacturers. In those idealistic times there seemed to be the Greater Good but when I saw an industry extinguished I lost respect for good intentions and became mildly suspicious of those who meant well.

Doing "Good"

Every man is guilty of all the good he didn't do. — Voltaire

The girl I had expected to marry had changed her mind as soon as my release from the Army was imminent and, assured by everyone that these things happen and reminded about all the available pebbles on all the beaches, I collected my small gratuity and left the country, as one does when seeking fresh starts and anxious to do good to the deprived. I could not be sure, though, how many new beginnings were allowed without it becoming unseemly.

Morocco, then not the tourist-friendly country it has become, diffused an air of mystery, particularly Fez, a city empty of visitors, where I had arranged to join a free clinic for the poor. It was cold as the spring was late and I roamed the streets of the old *medina* which was inundated by smells, some exciting as in the spice market while others, near the tanneries, were revolting, the vivid colours of the dyes barely compensating for the pungency of the animal skins.

Strains of Arabic music came from a house with a massive wooden door decorated with geometric carvings and metal studs, contrasting with the dilapidated state of the rest of the exterior. There was one small window set into the thick wall where I could see a man's face peering at me though he quickly came down dressed in livery.

Assuming I was a guest he kept bowing and ushering me inside until the master of the house appeared. Clothed in a pure white *djellaba* of such fine linen that it seemed transparent, he too insisted I come in, dismissing my apologies in perfect, if rather stylish, French and switching easily to equally excellent English.

"It's a party!" he said. "There are so few foreigners that you are a welcome addition."

He led me down a corridor to an indoor garden that opened to the surrounding reception rooms through elaborate arches. Orange and lemon trees grew through breaches in the tiled floor and the air was overwhelmingly perfumed as jasmine, trailing around the arches, was already in flower, and fragrant bushes grew in niches around a central fountain. A small group of Europeans, Americans and Moroccans milled about, drinking mint tea and fruit juices, which were passed around by servants wearing the same livery as the man who had opened the door.

Musicians played on a mezzanine holding the fiddles vertically, and there were drums as well as wind instruments of different sizes.

"Our forefathers brought the melodies with them from al-Andalus," *Si* M'hamed, as that was our host's name, said. "It's our *musique classique, quoi*?"

He took me to meet some English people, introducing me as the doctor from London, and got a quick response from an overweight man who said his name was Cutforth.

"I've just got up from a bad pneumonia but the BBC wanted this program and I couldn't turn the job down. Not in my position," he added darkly. "It will probably kill me!"

I told him that he was more likely to shake off a chest infection in Fez than in a damp and smoke-filled London but he looked dubious and insisted on writing down the address where I was staying. I could see that he was not going to let me go now that he had found a British doctor, however inexperienced.

"We are going to film the interior of the Karaouine mosque tomorrow," he said enticingly. "Do you want to come with us?"

I knew that foreigners were not allowed to enter and he was obviously pleased at my astonishment, winking vigorously as he leaned towards me conspiratorially.

"You have to understand how they run things here," he whispered in my ear. "All you need is a silky voice on the telephone saying: *On dit que Sa Majesté s'interesse.*"

Delighted with these words he kept repeating them in English using different versions, as if to see which sounded best.

"It is said that His Majesty is interested! They say that His Majesty is interested! One says that His Majesty interests himself! It is understood that His Majesty..."

But *Si* M'hamed had come to take me away again.

"Don't spend your time with a sick old man," he said. "Let me introduce you to someone your own age. This is Miss Cathy."

An American girl who wrote for a travel publisher specialising in cheap trips, Cathy took her work seriously, journeying from town to town in crowded local buses, donkey carts or camel trains, staying in lodgings that lacked running water or flush toilets, and it occurred to me that only a woman could be so scrupulous, testing everything personally. At the end of her assignment she had bought a second-hand car and planned to go to Ifni, a mysterious Spanish outpost on the west coast of Africa.

"No one I know has been there," she had replied when I asked why.

The following day I joined the BBC team at their hotel and found René Cutforth in good spirits. The cameraman claimed it had all been "psychological" as he had brightened up now that he had a doctor as part of his entourage and had convinced himself that I was a famous specialist.

Cathy arrived in a black *djellaba* that went down to her ankles. Her face was veiled, an over-reaction as when we got to the mosque and were asked to remove our shoes her toenails emerged painted immodestly red.

"Give me your socks," she said. "Hand them over!"

"I don't want to walk barefoot," I protested vainly. "I might catch verrucas!"

The white courtyard, symmetrical disposition of the columns and seemingly infinite rows of arches imparted a peculiar serenity, and the mosque's archivist and librarian said I could help with medical manuscripts until my clinic opened. He pointed out that the Karaouine had been founded in 859 CE, and was therefore the oldest place of learning in continuous existence in the world. I supposed that this must be true as at that time England was being fought over by the Vikings and by Saxon kings called Æthelbald, Æthelred and Æthelwulf. The librarian's smugness was not convincing, however, in view of the poor quality of his institution's present work, which made it an example of continuous decline, but I did feel there was something significant in studying where Maimonides and Leo Africanus had studied before me.

Cathy, an array of cameras hanging about her as though they were weapons, took photographs of the city, and during our walks together we came across an entirely blue man in the market. Clothed in a vivid indigo *burnous*, his face, though mostly hidden by a blue turban and veil, as well as his hands and feet, were all blue.

"It's just a blue man" was the only answer we could get to our questions and my new friend the librarian was not more helpful.

"These blue people are not of any consequence," he had said dismissively and even *Si* M'hamed had not much to add.

"They come up sometimes for the markets, in Marrakech rather than Fez," he had explained. "Why waste your time? Go to Casablanca, it's truly like Paris."

It was decided that I was to study medical documents from Moorish Spain that had been for a brief period in the possession of Christian monks. Untouched for hundreds of years, insects and rodents escaped in such numbers when I opened the boxes that I thought they would consume the contents faster than us scholars could look at them. I doubt that our work had any outcome though I still have the notes of what had interested me.

Each chapter in one medieval medical manuscript was headed by the phrase "*B'ism Allah al-rahman al-rahim*" or "In the name of God, the Clement, the Compassionate", which had been crossed off in red ink by monks. They had written above "*In the name of Jesus Christ, our Lord*" in Latin, only for it to be crossed off yet again when the book had been exchanged for hostages and the Muslims had tried to restore the original version.

The other note I made relates to a text published under the zealous Calif, al-Mansour. Ailments are described starting with the tongue, the most important organ, the author states, since it "allows us to recite verses from the *Koran*". Another edition, from more tolerant times, starts with the scalp and works its way down but, like the doctors who bowed before such prevailing winds, the librarian avoided discussing such unsafe subjects.

Much later, when I applied for a teaching hospital post at The Royal Free in London the story of my work in Fez had helped get me the registrar's job. John Ballantyne, the consultant who had interviewed me, used this as an example of his own good judgement for the rest of his long life. He had somehow come to believe over the decades that it was the Dead Sea scrolls that I had translated, a rumour he circulated despite my denials, and which I suspect led many surgeons to look upon me with disapproval if not contempt as intellectuals were not held in much regard. I learnt that many things are neither here nor there and people believe what happens to suit them at the time.

As the clinic had still not opened, Cathy offered to drive me through the remarkable Dadès Gorges and the Dra Valley as far as Zagora provided. I would then go with her to Ifni. I agreed, though her car seemed barely serviceable, and we set off into the desert.

Today the sights of Morocco illustrate travel brochures, though I believe that even now no one goes to Ifni, which is not far from Agadir. Cathy and I took it in turns to drive her frail car south of Goulimine before turning westwards.

We came across blue people from whom we bought camel's milk with dates and almonds, which seemed to be their main diet as Cathy, used to living off the land, had failed to bring provisions. We discovered that the blue colour was a dye that came off their garments. It felt waxy, like the carbon paper of old typewriters.

We watched a dance performed by women where the movements were restricted to the upper part of the body. Arms, neck and shoulders and particularly the hands and fingers carried out intricate rhythmic gestures to simple musical tones but, as neither the trunk nor legs took part, they danced sitting down. I have never seen or heard of anything like that.

The tracks we followed eventually got covered by sand, so we relied on the position of the sun to point us westwards until we heard shots and saw Moroccan soldiers waving and shouting "*Arrêtez!*"

We were in a minefield and had to be guided out as we were told that the whole frontier was mined. We never got to Ifni, and Cathy and I parted as I returned to Fez where the clinic had finally opened and she went on to cross the Sahara to Timbuktu, traveling again by bus, as her car was now a write-off. She gave me all the films she had taken to send to America when I returned to England, as the post in Africa was unreliable.

When I was back in England some months later Cathy called from America. She thanked me for sending her films, as she had been able to sell the pictures. She had not expected that I would send them and was very grateful.

"People don't bother," she said.

I met other young women like her and, perhaps attracted by that special character, I had tried to keep in touch when they moved on, but I do not know what became of any of them. I wonder if they are still slipping away, restlessly roving here and there. But this may be fantasy and they could all have exhausted whatever flame had fired them and settled down like the rest of us.

*

My desire to aid humanity was intense if vague, and there were then few organisations ready to satisfy young people's need to be of assistance to the deprived. I had been assigned to help Dr Triboulet, a Frenchwoman in her early 30's, just a few years older than me whose thick black hair was always trying to escape the clasp that held it in a bun.

I had met her briefly when I had spent a year as an undergraduate in Paris before going on to Medical School in London. A dedicated doctor, she had been associated with the *Prêtre Ouvrier*, or Worker Priest movement, a Catholic attempt to be part of the revolutionary factions so attractive to the young at the time.

She now handed me a white coat and told me to "do what you can", taking me by surprise as I had only worked in a structured environment. The line of patients waiting in the street was so long that it was impossible to see more than a fraction so a couple of male nurses, "*les infirmiers*", wandered among them dispensing advice and medicine.

An exhausted young woman who had walked for five days carrying a comatose child affected me particularly as I was convinced he had tuberculous meningitis and that he should be hospitalised.

"It is too late for any treatment now so they will only send them away," Dr Triboulet said. "Tell her there is nothing to be done and she will go. Pity it is a boy."

I had never seen such gross symptoms and signs and there was nothing minor except a number of girls with palpitation. They had all been recently married and the doctor assured them it was only "*Boomzooyi*" or something that sounded like that.

"Infertility is terribly serious," she said, "as the husband will take a second wife and she would be divorced or reduced to the position of a servant. The mother-in-law would try and get rid of her by treating her badly even if the husband is more compassionate."

My good intentions exasperated Dr Triboulet, especially when I said that I wanted to stay as I felt people in Africa needed me more than those in England.

"Don't you see that what we are doing is useless?" she said. "It just makes us feel good. Like Dr Schweitzer in Central Africa, we practice bad medicine. Do you want to help or enjoy the adulation of a few poor people? Go back to England, there are sick persons there and everyone is equally deserving!"

I had not been prepared for her outburst, though she had been moody for some time, and I said that I could send her antibiotics and vaccines.

"Have you not understood?" she said, shouting now. "There is no shortage. The problem is access. The disasters that inspire you so much are man-made, as one group wants to starve its neighbours to death. Then you turn up wide-eyed, anxious to save everybody from what you think are natural disasters and each group is too embarrassed to admit it is simply trying to exterminate the other."

I was unable to make sense of her gloomy philosophy and said that I just wanted to do something worthwhile. She was silent for a moment, then suggested I kill the king.

She was making a fool of me, and I said that there would always be another king.

"It might stir things up," she said. "Maybe a little good may come from it. Who knows?"

We are different people when young and I cannot imagine what impression I, too, might have made.

*

The last time I gave a talk in Paris I was approached by an old lady who had seen my name on the program. She was in her eighties, her white hair slipping out of an untidy bun.

"You don't remember me?" she said. "Lise? Lise Triboulet? The clinic in Fez? *Au Maroc, les années soixantes*?"

She insisted I come up to her flat round the corner from the old faculty, near the *Odéon*, and climbed the five flights of stairs easily while I was breathless and had to rest.

"I told the *gérant*," she said, "to put a notice with 'STAIRS REDUCE *LE CHOLESTEROL*' to encourage *les locataires*."

Unmarried, her life had been devoted to Africa but she had been happy to return to Paris unlike others, she said, who had been unable to tear themselves away from that continent.

I told her I admired all she had done and the sacrifices she had made and said I always had doubts about the direction I had given to my life, but she would have none of it.

"It is I who has regrets," she said ruefully. "When the first humans, hominids or whatever, left Africa only *les perdants*, what you call the losers, stayed behind. It is I who was wrong about everything!"

She seemed diverted rather than sorry or angry.

"Do you remember Morocco?" she said. "You wanted to help the poor, *les déshérités du monde*? Helping a few individuals was not enough and we all wanted to help 'The People' rather than actual persons. There was a Greater Need than need, like a Greater Good and a Greater Truth than truth. The communists were so sure they were right they became enforcers. Those well-meaning students we knew from distant countries can't explain the awful things they ended up doing in the name of the Greater Good. At least Catholics like me only had condom problems because old men in the Vatican were confused about sex."

She laughed and asked if I remembered the *Cercle Marxiste*.

"I went once or twice," I said. "Was it '51 or '52, just before I left?"

She wanted to know if I remembered Sar.

"Vaguely," I said. "Wasn't he that dim communist from Indochina?"

"*Cambodge*," she said. "From Cambodia. Later he was known as Pol Pot."

"Take care," she said, pecking me on both cheeks. "Hang on to the handrail, it is more difficult going down."

"Show yourself *de temps en temps*," she called down when I reached the bottom, adding as an afterthought, "it just seemed the right thing at the time!"

I never saw her again. The obituary praised her work in *Afrique Equatoriale Française* but did not say anything about Morocco. Perhaps they did not want to offend Muslim sensibilities by commending her missionary work.

Starting a Career

The secret of getting ahead is getting started. — Mark Twain

I had been warned that, contrary to popular belief, my army service would be of no account, and the time I had spent in Morocco "doing good" would also set me back as idealistic fantasy was then a matter for suspicion or ridicule rather than for respect.

I should have, everyone agreed, kept my "foot on the ladder" and "I had only myself to blame" if no one offered me a job. Studying ancient texts was "fooling around" so, with the despair of the unemployed, I put it about that my objective in North Africa had been to climb the Atlas Mountains as sporting challenges were better valued.

House Surgeon, the only post I could aspire to, was the most junior, and the only one I could get was at the Royal London Homeopathic Hospital. I knew nothing of homoeopathy but my work would involve only surgery and my finances had run out so neither I nor they, as I was the only applicant, had other options.

That hospital stands in Queen Square, between that for Nervous Diseases on one side and the Hospital for Sick Children behind it. Neither of these world-famous institutions had anything to do with the Homeopathic but their presence gave the area an international resonance, so when asked where I worked I could mumble "Queen Square" and if I did so almost under my breath it might hint at modesty rather than deceit.

The junior doctors were mostly from India or Pakistan as these posts were unlikely to advance any career in this country. Everyone struggled with higher qualifications, taking the examinations again and again at some cost while receiving scanty training and little supervision.

The Senior Surgical Registrar's first name contained too many syllables so we just called him by his surname, Patel. I have rarely assisted someone as deft and whose gentle manner applied also to his surgical technique. Each incision, gesture or placing of clamps and ligatures was so delicate that his instrument slipped in and out and seemed hardly to have been there at all. The best I could do was watch Patel and copy him.

The homeopathic physicians paid daily visits to the wards spending hours at the bedside discussing patients' complaints in detail, no matter how trivial and Patel, who said he was used to "funny medicine" in India, kept out of their way. Symptoms of little consequence, he said, were often those that caused the most distress and patients benefited from talking about them. It was for the surgeon to cure the patient, and then for a homeopath to discuss their concerns and treat them with preparations at infinitesimally small dilutions.

"Their drugs are not herbal remedies," he said, "as they dilute a substance in water and then dilute it again thousands of times till it is just water by our reckoning but they claim that an echo of the original stuff remains. The patient feels better whether it is the magic water or the interest they take and their intense concern in the minutiae of their symptoms. At least, they feel, someone cares about them."

The food provided for the resident staff was bad. Every now and again one of the exasperated doctors would suggest we "currify" it and threw the tasteless meat, vegetables, barely boiled potatoes or whatever we had been given into a large pot with curry powder and cooked it until any trace of the original flavour or texture had disappeared. I had never had Indian food before and I acquired a taste for curry, though for a while I saw it only as a way of disguising the inedible.

Many of the seriously ill emergencies we admitted were women who had had what was then known as "criminal septic abortion".

Termination of pregnancy was illegal and punishment mandatory, as implicated doctors would be forbidden to practice ever again and often appeared in novels as the flawed if brilliant characters that help fiction along as they drink their way to an African or Amazonian hell, or else as criminals motivated only by greed.

These laws, although present in most countries, were generally disregarded by enough doctors to become flexible while most authorities turned a formally disapproving blind eye. This was not the case in Britain where laws, just or unjust, are meticulously enforced so that it was marginal and unqualified persons operating in back rooms who performed abortions illegally. This resulted in infection and sometimes loss of life, so I regularly admitted women on the verge of death and stayed by their side all night.

I was not quite aware then that we were part of changes that would transform society, as we rarely see our times in such terms and they did not all take place simultaneously. The contraceptive pill was not yet on the market and our attitudes belonged to a culture that had just begun to disappear.

"Don't think about it too much or it may confuse you," Patel said. "Just remember that you can't marry all of them and take them home so you can care for them."

When Patel left we gave him a party.

"This is a crazy place and when you have become a reputed surgeon no one will believe you ever worked here," he told me, "but you have learnt more than you think. Just keep on diluting, maybe that is how life goes."

The old Homeopathic is now called "The Royal London Hospital for Integrative Medicine" and is part of University College London Hospital, and they aim to provide a "person-centred holistic approach". They offer advice on complementary and alternative therapies and respond to a definite need.

*

The Whittington, my next Hospital, was a hopeful amalgam; its name was the epitome of all fresh starts as it related to the apprentice who had failed to make his way in the London of the Middle Ages and was returning home with his cat as his only companion.

When he reached the village of Highgate, Dick Whittington heard the bells of the city calling him back, urging him to try again. Legend has it that he married the boss' daughter and became "thrice" Lord Mayor of London, so not only the site at the top of Highgate Hill was appropriate but its name also was inspiring. Some sort of health facility or hospice had been there for centuries until the Whittington, a fusion of three hospitals still separated by major roads, came into being with the National Health Service in 1948.

Optimism pervaded the hospital which, led by outstanding senior staff, attracted juniors, most of whom were to make a name for themselves. I believed that this new beginning in an enthusiastic atmosphere would set me on my road until I realised how bad the ENT department was.

From the start I was left to fend for myself as Dr Liu, the Chinese Registrar who was supposed to guide me, hardly spoke any English and the two consultants were rarely there and were quite uninterested in teaching me anything. I got the impression that they expected me to fail at everything and then disappear to some obscure and distant land so they could forget me completely.

Though Dr Liu was very amiable, I could not understand him and I never found out how he got through his clinic. The patients did not seem to mind perhaps because he examined them more thoroughly than most and there may often be nothing to say. Perhaps many did not speak English either and they communicated by gesture.

I followed him to the operating theatres to watch him do a list of children's tonsils and adenoids, and after the first case he indicated by signs that I could do the next one if I wished. I nodded vigorously as one does when speech is of little use, and scrubbed up to the dismay of the anaesthetist who had already put the second child to sleep. We waited as no one could find Dr Liu and I was afraid to start by myself, until a porter said he had seen him leave on his way to the cinema. I had no alternative but to do the next five cases unsupervised. I did them carefully and slowly and by good fortune nothing untoward happened. I thanked the anaesthetist who was preparing a formal complaint but now changed his mind, and that was how I started my career in ENT surgery.

I later discovered that Dr Liu spoke excellent French. And by chance French was also my first language so my life changed remarkably after that. We had long conversations both at work and at rest and I learnt a great deal from Gabriel Liu. We became good friends, though I never discovered anything about his life or even how he had come to speak French so well in China as he only laughed when I asked. He never wanted to know anything about me either, so ours remained a strange encounter and despite the months spent together and everything he taught me we just said goodbye when we parted and I never saw him again.

*

After Dr Liu's departure I felt grimly on my own, as the two consultants came to do their clinics and their operating lists, which I imagined they did adequately, but made no attempt to teach me anything and gave me the impression that they regarded my questions as an intrusion. If I asked why they carried out a particular procedure they seemed puzzled, as though it was none of my business.

I was misled by the Casualty doctors into admitting a bus conductor one night. He was definitively rather sick but his illness, whatever it was, had only a vague connection with my specialty. Perhaps a slight sore throat among many other symptoms but no one else wanted to take him. He went downhill quickly despite negative tests and the various specialists I called had no explanation so I began to fear he might just die. My chiefs, as usual, annoyed at my having admitted him kept away, avoiding responsibility.

The man's wife believed that a malign spell had been cast on him and wanted to take him back to Jamaica for exorcism. I tried to dissuade her but he was so obviously deteriorating that I must have sounded less and less convinced, and as my bosses were desperate to get rid of him before he died undiagnosed, I wrote a detailed report and urged her to take him straight to a hospital in Kingston.

I did not hear anything for a while as I had left the Whittington but the letter had followed me from place to place covered with helpful suggested addresses.

It was from some sort of Witch Doctor who addressed me as 'Dear colleague' thanking me for the referral. The spell, cast by a venomous neighbour, had been exorcised and the man was now fully recovered.

*

I had been right that time but this was not always the case as when I admitted an old lady. Living on her own, she suffered from malnutrition so I sent for her daughters and, with the strong views that overwhelmed me at the age of 26, I lectured them. Fortunately I cannot remember my words as recalling them would leave me abashed, though I do remember accusing them of neglecting their mother.

The three daughters who had come with their husbands kept silent as I harangued them but one of the husbands caught me in the corridor when I had finished. He said that their mother had abandoned them when young and even now, despite all their efforts, had no interest in them or their children. She was, he said, a bad woman by any standard.

"Remember," he said, "that the hooligans who mug you in the street are the dear old pensioners of tomorrow and they won't have changed one little bit. No one does."

*

Another day I extracted a foreign body from a man's gullet, the first time I had done that and of course with no supervision. It is a delicate operation and dangerous for the inexperienced but, as usual, I had been left to do it alone. The object, which the patient said he had swallowed when trying to clear food caught in a tooth, was a half-crown, a large coin worth two shillings and sixpence which, after circulating for 500 years, was demonetised in 1970. Our biggest coin was just too big to pass down to the stomach.

I was so pleased at my success in extracting it endoscopically under anaesthetic that I handed the half-crown back to the patient with a flourish the following morning as he lay in bed in full view of the ward and nurses and he promptly swallowed it again.

"Why did you do that?" I asked.

"I don't know why I do it," he said blandly.

I still do not understand what lies behind such things though I have thought a lot about it and the various theories that have been offered in explanation.

*

Some patients seemed quite complex, like the woman who complained that she had swallowed a fish bone that had remained stuck in her throat.

"Thirteen years," she replied when I asked how long it had been there.

I tried to explain that it was not possible.

"I know," she said patiently. "I know what you mean. The fishbone, a thin needle of cartilage, rots and dissolves over time, no?"

I nodded but she went on to say that there are other fish bones that just dig in.

"No, much worse," she replied when I asked if that was the one. "Do you know the backbone? With hooks on either side? That's the one!"

I agreed to examine her throat under the anaesthetic on the condition that she let me call the psychiatrist if it was clear, so when I did find nothing I wrote a long and detailed referral.

The psychiatrist came to see her but did not send for me. I heard nothing more and I suspected he was avoiding me. The nurse explained that he was going to fetch his mother.

"His mother?" I asked. "Are you sure that's what he said? His own mother?"

The nurse was adamant that the psychiatrist wanted to bring his mother to see the patient and, with Freud in mind, I thought it was bizarre.

He was hardly more helpful when he finally agreed to speak to me, though only on the telephone. He thought the woman's story was very funny and laughed as he recalled the details. When I demanded action he said she was not harming anybody and suggested I should not have operated on her. He asked what I wanted from him, to redirect her anxieties to the war in Vietnam?

"Or," he went on, "do you just want her to spare your department and annoy other surgeons? The gynaecologists perhaps?"

I discovered that his mother was a well-known psychiatrist and that it was they who had revealed that the illness of King George III may have been porphyria. I regret not having had the chance of meeting them both properly. I also saw the patient briefly many years later when I sat in my own rather grand clinic at Guy's Hospital surrounded by my students. She recognised me despite the years that had passed.

"Oh, it's you!" she said, and walked straight out again.

*

I remember vividly every mistake I made, and the anxiety brought on by lack of help and guidance has never left me completely.

The neurosurgical registrar called me one night to see a man who required immediate surgery as an ear abscess was ready to burst into his brain, and I called my chief at once, but I must have looked dismayed as I put down the phone.

"He told you to go ahead by yourself, didn't he?" the neurosurgeon asked. "He is not coming, is he?"

"He told me to be careful," I said defensively, as I felt responsible for my department and embarrassed for my chief who had no intention of coming.

I had never even seen such an operation bordering inside the skull, and I had no idea what to do so the neurosurgeon suggested I practice on a cadaver in the mortuary as no one minded what you did with the dead then, provided you tidied them up afterwards.

I had recently acquired a manual, but real anatomy looks different from the line drawings and the spindly little sketches seemed unrelated to the bleeding, swollen tissues I saw before me.

A nurse read out instructions from the book as I operated, though they were often misleading without the right instruments, yet somehow I drained the abscess. I should have stopped there but I damaged the facial nerve in my excess of zeal when I tried to clear up all the disease. I did not even have an operating microscope and the patient woke up with that side of his face paralysed. The neurosurgeon told him that he owed his life to me, which I suppose was true as I had spared him a brain abscess, so he was grateful and wanted to kiss my hand, which I hastily withdrew. I still feel bad when I recall that episode and today it would be called negligence to abandon a junior house officer in this way.

"I told you to be careful!" was all my chief had said.

Even though I had saved his life, irresponsible people had placed me in a situation which was beyond me, and though I never quite recovered it left me determined to learn from the best, so I went wherever I could to find them and that is how, years later, I visited a famous German professor in Tübingen.

He was both skillful and imaginative as I watched him carry out a delicate manoeuver that I had not seen before. I asked respectfully if he had done that because he was afraid to damage the facial nerve, which had remained such a source of anxiety for me.

He stopped as everyone in the operating theatre froze, mouths open in mid-utterance as when a video is put on pause. Silence was total and the atmosphere icy for a fraction of a second.

"I am never afraid of the facial nerve!" he spat out in fury.

His words were terse but the look he gave me, his expression intensified over a theatre mask, as well as the tone of his voice, implied profound contempt. I apologised, explaining that I was always afraid of causing damage but he waved me away with a sneer.

My anxieties compelled me to become expert at repairing surgical damage and I taught my own students to be so meticulous that, as far as I know, none of them has ever injured that particular nerve.

Courage may be as valuable as caution in a surgeon but preparation and practice should mitigate the risks.

*

Injuries to the facial nerve became less common as training improved but as I was gradually becoming an expert more patients were sent to me in the hope that I might repair such damage. The referrals came in a variety of manners and represented strangely different attitudes.

At one extreme the patient was suing the surgeon and seemed so vindictive towards him that I questioned it, explaining to him that he could not possibly win as facial nerve damage was a known risk of some ear operations. Why not just let me do my best to repair it and leave it at that?

"I just want to cause him as much trouble as I possibly can!" he replied.

It turned out that he realised half his face was paralysed when he woke up from the anaesthetic and asked what had happened but the nurses would not say. When the house surgeon finally appeared he confirmed that the nerve had been damaged and said that it would never, ever get better. The surgeon who was responsible refused to speak to him and, during the five days he remained on the ward, never appeared there.

"I wanted to ask him what had happened," he said, "that's all."

He had been bundled into an ambulance and taken to Guy's Hospital, for which he was very grateful but just wanted to speak to the surgeon responsible for what had happened.

Another patient was the opposite extreme as the surgeon had come with him in the ambulance, insisted on assisting in the repair operation and then came to see him every day until he was discharged. The patient became quite devoted to him.

I hoped my students realised that we are all aware that surgeons cannot be infallible. We simply want to know that our doctors care about what happens to us.

*

Very junior doctors such as myself were expected to stay in the hospital even when not on duty, so when I lacked companions I read.

I read that in the 17th century when the French King Louis XIV developed an anal fistula, they brought in the leading doctors in consultation. The physicians suggested baths of various sorts, while the surgeons, who were considered of a lower academic status, recommended an operation. The king decided to try the baths first and if that failed the leading surgeon, Charles-Francois Felix, would be called upon to intervene.

Felix, who also attended to the poor at the free public hospitals, insisted on performing all the fistula operations himself so that by the time he came to the King his skills had been honed to a maximum proficiency as well as speed, essential when there was no anaesthetic.

His success not only established the operation as the most effective treatment but transformed the status of surgery and Felix himself was ennobled, raising the prestige of all surgeons.

I began to practice all the time.

*

Whenever I watched an operation I read it up in manuals of surgery, I borrowed the instruments and set up a simulacrum of the operating field, and then I practised each step again and again.

I did this for the rest of my life and never performed an operation that I had not done before without first getting hold of the instruments, setting them up and repeating all the gestures required many times. I made my students do this too and when one asked why we also did this with our eyes shut, I said it was to copy the military who load their weapons blindfolded, then I said it was in case we go blind, hoping to get a laugh from a rather tired audience, but the true reason is simple. First it trains our coordination so our visual sense is always supported by an underlying dexterity which we need not even be aware of, and secondly subconscious deftness can be helpful in the split second that the visual field might be obscured by a gush of blood.

The first time I was taught to practise seriously was when I was a medical student in my first clinical year. Harold Ellis, then the registrar who eventually became a well-known teacher and distinguished professor of surgery, had made me stay behind and practice tying surgical knots.

"When you start your training as a surgeon," he insisted as I must have seemed bored by the repetition, "they won't tell you to go ahead and do the operation. They will ask you to tie a knot or a suture as it is easier from your side of the operating table, and if you do it expertly and slickly without hesitation they will let you do more."

That lesson proved useful on many occasions. When I became a registrar at the Royal Free Hospital I watched the excellent surgeon, John Groves, perform an operation on the ear. He made a tiny prosthesis out of a platinum wire wrapped round a small bead of fat as pre-packed replacement body parts were not yet easily available. He said that maybe next time he might try letting me do it.

When that time came I had already spent hours practising under the microscope so that when he told me to make a prosthesis I did it so quickly that he asked me to make another one while he watched. He said nothing.

Later I heard him tell the anaesthetist that some people just have an innate gift. "This young chap had only seen me do it once and then made two perfect prostheses for me as though he had done it hundreds of times!" Which indeed I had.

My wife Gill and I were on holiday with a friend, the great pianist Maurizio Pollini and his wife, staying at the Pensione Serena near Pesaro in Italy where he had had a piano installed so that he could practice for a few hours every day. When we finally heard him perform, it was with such spontaneity and freshness that no one could have imagined the preparation he had put into it. I asked if he always practised so assiduously for every performance, however familiar he might be with the piece.

"Always," he replied.

The Nose

Memories, imagination, old sentiments, and associations are more readily reached through the sense of smell than through any other channel.
— Oliver Wendell Holmes

At the very start of my training, when I was a Registrar at the Royal Free Hospital, I wrote a book called *The Sense of Smell and its Abnormalities.* It might have been a better book had I waited a few years but there was no other work on the subject, and I have figured as an expert on olfaction ever since.

Not long after its publication when I was still working in a junior capacity, I was approached by a rather withdrawn, shy individual who said he was a chemist working for a large conglomerate that sold odoriferous chemicals to manufacturers of scented soaps, deodorants, shampoos as well as sprays that give the smell of leather to the interior of new cars.

His company had faced financial loss as well as unending disputes when clients complained that despite analyses of the products the actual smell was still not quite right. These disputes often went to arbitration where opposing sniffers gave differing opinions.

My visitor had found that by analysing the gases which hovered over the surface rather than the liquid itself they could save a great deal of money. The company was anxious to compensate him and what he requested was that they fund him to do a PhD on the sense of smell.

Having read my book he asked me to be his supervisor, which startled me as I was not ready to oversee anybody. I was not even entitled to do so as it would be a few years before I would be a recognised "Teacher" at

London University, but he was so persistent that he managed to persuade my own chief to supervise me and so, by proxy, his work.

I suggested he approach a professor at University College, a Nobel Laureate, and in due course he was invited to meet him while I was increasingly uneasy at the responsibility imposed on me. I wished he would simply go away and leave me alone.

His meeting was successful as he was interviewed by three distinguished professors, all of them Nobel Laureates. When I asked for details he was embarrassed and it took a while before he confessed they had said: "If you come and work in our laboratory with all our things you can achieve in six months what would take you three years working with Mr Douek."

He vowed that he would not even consider it as he was committed to me, and it was a while before I convinced him that he could not possibly refuse their offer.

When years later I had my own unit at Guy's Hospital he reappeared having achieved his doctorate and insisted on joining my team. This time I had no problem as he was now a distinguished olfactory scientist and I was only too pleased to add him to our group.

I had felt honoured to have my name mentioned, even if only disparagingly, by not one but three Nobel Laureates. After all, it does not happen often.

*

I had wanted to describe how air flows through the nose in my book and I had assumed we all 'knew' that as surgeons had been operating on the airway for more than a century, but I discovered this information was the result of studies made 300 years ago using long-surpassed techniques.

I wrote to companies and institutes with facilities for measuring airflow hoping for guidance but only one bothered to reply. Lucas Industries, a name I knew from car batteries, seemed obliging and invited me to visit their facility in Cheshire. The enthusiasm of their reception became overwhelming when I arrived at the station, as although I had not even explained the nature of my quest a Rolls Royce was waiting.

"The Chief Engineer is very excited to meet you," the uniformed driver said, "after reading about the liver transplant in the papers today!"

I felt even more embarrassed when I was greeted by a group of engineers and scientists who introduced themselves by stating their impressive qualifications. The Chief Engineer, clearly an authoritarian who gave the impression that he was quick-tempered and did not suffer fools, offered to show me around to see what they could do.

He took me to a series of hangars, the first of which was huge and contained the model of a nuclear power station. I think it was Calder Hall or Dungeness and he told me, very proudly, that they had mapped the flow, both of liquids and gases, in all the cylinders and intricate piping of that magnificent structure, one of the first commercial nuclear power stations in the world. We then went to see the *Concorde* turbo jet engine and again the Chief Engineer explained the technology used to analyse the direction and turbulence of the flow of air and gases as they passed through that elaborate and complex machine. It towered over me and, taken aback by its size, I was even more unnerved at the thought that I would now have to explain that what had brought me there was so paltry as the air passing in and out through the nose.

We went on to other major projects before he ushered me into the boardroom where everyone looked at me in anticipation and again mentioned the liver transplant which had featured in the papers that morning but which had little to do with me and no connection with my project. I cannot imagine what they thought I was going to ask of them.

I felt obliged to tell them something about liver transplantation, though my only role had come when the director of the Liver Unit had asked me to perform a tracheostomy on his first patient. Professor Roger Williams had not mentioned that there was a problem with anticoagulation and his team watched with what I imagined was contempt, barely hidden by their surgical masks, my difficulties in trying to stop the bleeding.

I did not mention that detail, and I went on quickly to show the engineers the plastic moulds I had made of the nasal cavity.

The room went quiet when I explained my request, aware that it was trifling by comparison with their work, and I could see the Chief Engineer's face reddening so I expected only anger at the minor nature of my project, the fact that there was no money to pay for any studies and that I had only hoped for some advice.

He was finding it difficult to control himself but after a few moments of silence he appeared to pull himself together.

"You mean to say," he spluttered, "you mean to say that you fellows operate on the nose, altering its structure, without even knowing how the air flows through it?"

"It's not entirely like that," I said, bewildered by this turn of events. "Experience, practice, you know."

"No I don't know!" he spat out and told me that he himself was due to have an operation on his nose done in Manchester by Mr Harrison the following week.

I said that Mr Harrison was a very good surgeon but the Chief Engineer insisted we work on my project till late that night. He had the whole department measuring the flow of air through the nose when we breathe freely as well as when obstructed and filmed it all.

He was so happy with the results he drove me to the station himself and said he would send a copy of our findings to Mr Harrison the following morning.

"It was lucky you came," he said. "At least I am sure he will know what he is doing when he operates on my nose."

*

Most of my contemporaries were anxious to learn how to do "nose jobs". I guess we thought it would be fun and I had come near to it when I was still a Senior House Officer at the Whittington.

I had finished my afternoon chores and was on my way to the cinema when I was called back to admit a patient for the plastic surgeon. Such moments are the curse of the young doctor's life as they make them late for everything. Although anxious to go I had to take the girl's blood pressure and listen to her chest but she was too shy to remove her top.

"I don't have much time," I said. "I listen to chests all day, that is what I do. If you don't let me they won't do the operation."

The nurse called me back from the hospital gate as the patient had agreed to lift her top an inch at a time and then I hurried away but again the nurse stopped me.

"She wants to give you these," she said, handing me some photographs of Kim Novak, a beautiful actress popular at the time. "That is what she wants to look like."

"But they are only going to do the bump on her nose," I said.

I abandoned the cinema and called the plastic surgeon to tell him that his patient expected to look like Kim Novak.

"Oh my God, she wants to be someone else!" he said. "Better cancel the operation and ask the psychiatrist to talk to her."

I realised that there was more to cosmetic surgery and that if you did it you had to do it well, and to do any surgery well you have to do a lot of it. I decided to take a different path so I did not do nose jobs.

*

"When I breathe my nose whistles. It is very embarrassing."

The young woman was slim, good-looking and expensively dressed. Her toddler and the nanny waited outside as they were going somewhere afterwards and this was in my private rooms in Harley Street. By then I was a Consultant at Guy's and I recognised the signs.

"Sniffing cocaine," I said. "It is very difficult to graft the hole in your nasal septum and you will have to stop using or it will all fall apart at once."

"But it is part of our lifestyle!" she cried in despair. "My husband uses! He works in the City. All our friends use and I want to be like them!"

I said I could make the hole bigger so that it would not whistle. But then, I added, the nose might collapse eventually.

She decided she wanted me to repair it and the graft did take. I never saw her again so I never found out what became of their lifestyle.

Training

The things we have to learn before we can do, we learn by doing. — Aristotle

My proper training started as a Registrar at the Royal Free Hospital. Since then I have only worked with outstanding people to whom I owe any skill that I have acquired and also the support that has allowed me to indulge my curiosity about nature and disease. My teachers and companions helped me participate in research and discovery.

The Royal Free Hospital stood in Grays Inn Road, in central London, but had outposts in Hampstead where it would eventually move. For a long time it was unique in training women doctors, although by the time I had got there many of the staff were men as well as half the students. Nevertheless a certain echo of the pioneering women resonated and gave me a special way of looking at things. I have actively favoured the promotion of women and encouraged my nieces and great-nieces to consider medicine as a profession. I suspect that may also have had something to do with my time there.

On my first day, while sauntering distractedly along the corridors I came across a bevy of female medical students led by an imperious woman who ran into me and pushed me against the wall.

"Who are you?' she asked.

She ordered me to present a case at the Grand Round the following Friday and when I appealed to my chiefs, Mr Ballantyne and Mr Groves, that as a newcomer I was not ready to present anything, they said that there was no way out. When Sheila Sherlock, the first female Professor of Medicine and a world expert on liver disease, told you to present a case you did what you were told.

When my turn came I was subjected to a traumatic third degree by her and her assistants, though members of the ENT department tried to support me as best they could. Everything I said was minutely questioned and every decision we had made debated, but I was told that I had acquitted myself adequately and that Professor Sherlock was pleased. She now expected me to present once a month.

These Grand Rounds taught me how to question every option, to explain why a diagnosis was made and the reason for every course of action. There is no place for vagueness in good medicine. These regular meetings are a sign of the quality of a teaching hospital.

At Guy's we also had a meeting every week to discuss cases that had remained a mystery or gone wrong. We called them formally "Morbidity and Mortality" and we discussed every patient in detail, but informally we referred to these meetings as "Death and Disaster". I sat by Omar Shaheen, the cancer surgeon, and when we listened at how our assistants had battled vainly against an inescapable death we whispered to each other as when we were at the English School together in Cairo, Egypt: "Where we came from they would have said it was fate!"

When my own time came, so many decades later, to be a patient at the Royal Free, it had moved to Hampstead and I saw that the world-famous Liver Centre she had set up had been renamed after her. I could not resist telling the young doctor who admitted me that I had known Sheila Sherlock. He looked puzzled as that was the name of a Centre, not a person. I dropped the subject.

*

I quickly learnt how to do the first operation which could restore normal hearing. It is called stapedectomy and had been shown on television performed for the first time in England by surgeons at King's College Hospital under the title of 'Your Life in Their Hands', and it was also one of the first hailed as 'Spare Part Surgery'. It was the starting point of all the surgeries for deafness.

Few had any aptitude for intricate surgery using the new Zeiss microscope. Progress always leaves people behind, and perfectly good surgeons unable to learn new skills were pushed aside. Many accepted this gracefully and referred their patients to others, turning an ability to select the best man for a particular job into an expertise of its own. Too embarrassed or too proud to acknowledge their inadequacies, others failed to inform patients when something could be done for them, or worse, attempted what they were not capable of doing, sometimes with catastrophic results.

I realised that the only way to avoid being left behind as we age is by specialising continually and doing only the surgery we feel we can still do better than others. That was what I tried to do when my turn came and though the number of operations I undertook diminished as I got older, I never lost the confidence that my patients had the best chance available. When young I put those thoughts aside, however, and concentrated on the exciting enterprise ahead.

Stapedectomy restores hearing lost through a common hereditary condition called otosclerosis. The tiniest bone in the body, the stapes or stirrup of the middle ear, is defective, does not vibrate freely and has to be replaced by a minute 'spare part'.

When at last I was allowed, under close supervision, to do a stapedectomy by myself I had reached the front line of modern surgery.

The patient had been an 83-year-old woman who was so deaf that hearing aids did not help anymore. She had had six children and, as usual in that condition, her hearing had deteriorated with each pregnancy so it was murmured that if I failed it could hardly be worse and that may have been why they had let me do the operation.

She did well, her hearing virtually normal, so I became attached to her as one does to one's early successes.

I learned not to dismiss the elderly only because of age as I saw how she enjoyed being able to hear. Forty years later I did a similar operation on a woman in her 80's in the face of claims that it had been unnecessary as she had died less than two years later. Her daughter wrote to say how much her mother had benefited even though her time had been short. Pleased with her good hearing, that woman had attended a family wedding in Canada, which she would have avoided had she remained deaf. She had spoken to many relatives not seen for years and the operation had been worthwhile if only for that.

An unexpected outcome of my first stapedectomy had involved a family pact. The old lady's children and grandchildren had inherited her deafness, which made her feel guilty and she had offered to have the pioneering surgery as a trial run on their behalf. Now they all wanted to have it done in the same place and by the same person, and it made no difference when I explained that I was the most inexperienced member of the team. Intrigued, my chiefs encouraged me to operate on the 13 members of that family.

After doing that I was quite good at microscopic surgery.

*

I was desperate to do research, though I was not sure what it meant and my ideas were probably closer to fantasy. Sometimes words inspire even if their meaning largely escapes us, and I think this might have been the case as 'research' stirred in me emotions of seeking and exploring, perhaps similar to those that urge people more physically adept to climb mountains or discover distant lands. Though mine would have to remain a journey of the mind it would still be an exploration of sorts.

The ENT surgeons of my time avoided scientific investigation so there was no one to guide me while operative surgery, on the other hand, was making extraordinary progress and attracting the most creative minds.

I decided to investigate the sense of smell, which few had studied, and that was how I produced my first paper in the *Journal of Otology and Laryngology*.

Mr Groves had made me rewrite it eight times, but ended up by deciding that maybe the fourth version was the best after all. I have remained grateful to him for making me do it again and again as he showed me how criticism should be anticipated and faced in advance.

As a result of the interest it created I was asked to write my book on the sense of smell.

*

The time had come for promotion to Senior Registrar, the final step and the most important in a career as that would be the end of my years of training. After that I would be in charge of my own department and, for better or worse, I would be on my own. This meant that there was much discussion as to which department would offer me the best training for my last few years.

It was generally accepted that I should aim for King's College Hospital in Denmark Hill and I had the opportunity to apply for that.

*

My published paper attracted a good deal of attention and Mr Ballantyne had encouraged me to write my book, yet when the time came for me to apply he suggested we play down my research, my book and everything I was so proud of. The surgical world, he believed, could not yet accept that anyone might be both academically inclined and a good surgeon.

"It is either or," he insisted. "We will tell them you are a reliable surgeon as, deep in their hearts, they really want someone to mind the shop."

I had never met any of the four consultants who interviewed me at King's. There was Mr Lewis, a fine if self-effacing cancer surgeon, Mr Edwards who was very clever and very skilful and, of course, Mr Mawson and Mr Ludman whose textbook was all I had had to rely on at the Whittington Hospital.

As a result of an oversight for which the others blamed Mr Edwards, they had all booked their holidays at the same time. Did I feel I could cope by myself?

"To mind the shop," Mr Mawson added. "So to speak."

They looked relieved when I said there would be no problem, though it appeared that there was yet another thing. The Registrar was untrained and could not be relied on. Was I happy with that?

Mr Mawson walked me to the door trying to be more encouraging.

"By the way," he said, "you will be teaching Miss World."

"Miss who?"

One of the students had won the Miss World 1966 beauty contest and Mr Mawson thought, in compensation perhaps, for what they had burdened me with, it might be something for me to look forward to. She was Reita Faria, who turned out to be an excellent student and has made a good doctor. It remains one of those inconsequential things that add colour, that among the many things that I have done in a long life, I had at one time also taught Miss World.

*

A few days after I started at King's College Hospital, I heard Mrs Sim's name mentioned as well as her hospital, St Giles, and it was whispered with dismay. The consultants handled her existence and her hospital like a family secret, until a manager told me that I was expected to replace her for a few days, though I had never heard of St Giles Hospital and did not see how her holidays could have anything to do with me.

It turned out that King's was to absorb St Giles, a strategy imposed by nameless officials that may well have been sensible except for certain delicate matters that seemed meaningless to most though crushing to others. Those who had achieved eminence in the teaching hospitals found it hard to welcome the lesser colleagues, who were to join them as equals. Consultants were consultants, after all, and there was no mechanism to distinguish between them.

Mrs Sim did mainly tonsil operations, responding to a vast waiting list. If they closed down her unit patients would be waiting years for their operations and the press would hound those responsible. It was all very well King's doing fancy surgery on TV but as far as politicians were concerned it was the waiting list that mattered.

"Cancer patients die whatever you do, don't they?" a manager told me. "What's a couple of years here and there? As for deafness, you can always give them a hearing aid while they wait."

I did not know where St Giles was and kept Mrs Sim's little team of anaesthetist, nurse and porter waiting as traffic is heavy in south London. In the past they had simply cancelled operations and taken the day off when anyone was away, and now I, the intruder, was not even on time. They resented amalgamation with an internationally famous institution that would expose their cozy little life to the world.

Things got more difficult when I could not stop the bleeding in the first child who was aged seven, a situation that soon turned into a nightmare.

"How long will you be?" the little group kept asking. "We can't go on all day."

When the haemorrhage finally stopped I went on to the next case only to be told that the first little girl had started bleeding again.

"Bring her back," I said as soon as I had finished the second operation.

And so it went on. I started a blood transfusion as she continued to bleed, and at the end of that awful morning I went to reassure her mother before she saw the bottle of blood hanging over her child.

"Everything is fine!" I began, but her strange lack of response made me suspicious and I asked if the child had bled before.

"She always bleeds," she said. "She had a transfusion when they pulled out her tooth. We all bleed."

She had denied any such family tendency on admission and looked at me brazenly.

"You wouldn't have done the operation if you had known we were bleeders, would you?"

I took a specimen of blood to 'Rasputin', the haematologist at King's. I am not sure whether we called him that because he was so difficult or because he saw himself as the King of Haemophilia. He now looked at me scornfully.

"You didn't do the operation properly," he said. "That's why she bled!"

He showed me a map of south London with different coloured stars scattered here and there and pointed to each in turn with dramatic gestures.

"Christmas Factor! Factor IX deficiency! Haemophilia!" he shouted, picking up a long wooden pointer as though he was going to hit me, but it was only to reach a green star stuck above the others, somewhere in Bromley I think, as for some reason the map was upside down.

"Factor X!" he said, hitting the green star with the pointer. "Factor X! I have every single bloody abnormality south of the river here on my map, and you bring me this? You can't stop the bleeding so you blame an inherited defect! When you cut people they bleed and you don't control it because you are incompetent."

In due course that family of bleeders in Peckham was shown up, quietly hiding from the haematologists until I had flushed them out, but Rasputin accused me of having kept them from him.

"Factor V!" he yelled. "In Peckham! Why didn't you let me know before?"

*

When Mrs Sim confessed that she only felt confident doing tonsillectomies, I had protected her from exposure of her inadequacies by arranging for her to do only the tonsils, but few patients turned up and I called to apologise one afternoon when no one had come for her operating list.

"Never mind," she said. "It's not your fault, I'll see if I can get my hair done."

This happened so often that I wrote to the patients on the St Giles waiting list and, of those who bothered to reply, many said they had had their operation already. Their names had not been removed so the waiting list lengthened, satisfying everyone as it proved that her services were badly needed while the wards gained spare beds for emergencies when patients failed to turn up. Theatres were not strained by working at overfull capacity and Mrs Sim was grateful for the occasional free time. Not understanding how delicately structures hang together, I wanted to bring in efficiency but such well-meaning efforts often wreck fragile systems that just about function.

The story of my phantom waiting list got around as my opposite number at St Bartholomew's Hospital called offering to buy the St Giles tonsil list. It could be done officially, he said, as to transfer a waiting list might be seen as creative thinking in the NHS. When I explained that it was a fictitious list he claimed that many useful things, such as money, were only symbols and perhaps the same applied to waiting lists; they could be seen as a symbol of need.

"I got the idea from a Russian novel by Gogol," he said. "Land was priced according to the number of serfs so the landowners registered births but never deaths and values rose and rose. Everyone did well until some honest fool blew the whistle, the bubble burst and they were all ruined."

I did not accept his offer to buy my waiting list but my colleague achieved great eminence. I believe he may even have treated members of the Royal Family.

*

I sometimes received begging or threatening letters asking to bypass the waiting list. One was from a Labour Member of Parliament who wrote highly regarded articles on education in the *New Statesman* where his particular flair was unmasking middle-class schemes to get into the best schools and although my own children were still young, I read his articles with approval.

He asked, on House of Commons notepaper, for his daughter's operation to be brought forward because of repeated illness and missed schooldays, and enclosed a letter from her teacher. I showed it to a fellow Senior Registrar as we rummaged around our respective waiting lists.

"Bring her in!" he said. "Always bow to authority and influence. She is only a little girl who needs surgery, not the frontline of your battle for fairness!"

That colleague also ended up with a knighthood and the presidency of one of our Royal Colleges.

*

Roland Lewis guided me through cancer operations and we worked well together. His combination of modesty and fearlessness let him undertake new techniques without hesitation and he taught me not to be afraid to quietly stretch the limits of surgery. Bill Edwards was an eclectic teacher who also urged me to extend the range of what I could do and sent me to Oxford to watch a surgeon called Mr Livingstone. Mawson and Ludman had great reputations, and knowing that my teachers were preeminent gave me the comfort of believing that no one offered a better service and my patients could do no better by going anywhere else in the world. I have tried to keep abreast of every new development so that I could continue to feel the same confidence.

Stuart Mawson was slow and took two hours to finish an operation that Harold Ludman would complete in half the time but their results were equally good, though at first I could not work out the reason for the time difference so I recorded everything they did as I watched and I think no one noticed my note-taking.

The answer was simple as Ludman took each step systematically and in the same order while Mawson ambled around the operating field as if he was going for a walk. By temperament I was more like Ludman so I planned my techniques even more. Surgery involves facing the unexpected but that is easier to do when carefully prepared so I planned my operations in steps.

I must have contributed something at King's as they helped get me on the staff of Guy's Hospital and Mrs Sim gave me the tonsil set from St Giles when they closed it down. '*St Giles Hospital*' was engraved on the instruments and I handed them on to my successor who had never heard of the place and wondered how I had got hold of such sturdy if ancient tools. I suspect he never used them.

*

"You the research chap?" the voice on the telephone was only a whisper and vaguely mysterious.

"I am the ENT Senior Registrar," I said.

"That's it, that's the one we were told!"

The voice now sounded conspiratorial and suggested I go to the computer room right away if I was interested.

"Didn't know we had one," I said, quite excited. "Where is it?"

It was behind the car park, well away from everything else. A large Port-a Cabin, it stood on its own and I remember there was a lot of space inside with many stacks containing spools of tape. A small group of technicians wearing white coats explained that the hospital had set them up to help anyone who needed computing power which, they insisted, was the future of medicine. Literally everything will depend on computers and they had been waiting there to be of help but no one had come to ask them anything. They had been advised to "outreach" and that is why they had called me. "Can we help you?" they asked.

I was taken unawares by the suddenness of it all but I did not want to miss anything so I asked for help with a study I was doing and they wanted to know how many cases I had in mind.

"That's not many," one of them said, looking pained. "We can process thousands, even tens of thousands."

"Actually hundreds of thousands," another technician added. "You'd be better off using punch cards."

I did not return as I was mortified and it was only when I had become head of my own Hearing Research Group at Guy's that I had the courage, or the need, to touch a computer again. That was to add up electrical responses, thousands of them, and I understood how it worked. I found quite a large early French computer abandoned in the corridors which could be carted along on wheels. As no one could tell me who it belonged to I locked it up in my room for protection and announced that anyone could use it on request. Only one person did.

In time, when visiting residents came from abroad, we had so many computers that I was not sure of the number and an American seeing the old French machine said they still used one of those for billing. The Russian shrugged as they had nothing like that where he came from so I gave it to him but he refused to take it. He said it was not like that in the Soviet Union as he would have to hand it over to a central organisation when he got back and it would probably remain there in storage forever.

*

My training was now technically over and the moment had come for me to apply for my own department, my own assistants and my own trainees and students. It was time for me to become a Consultant.

Something separates the surgeon from other doctors and especially academics as we are also part of the world of manual workers, of those who are skillful with their hands. We have something in common with tailors, mechanics and carpenters and though, like the physicians and scientists, we have had to absorb a huge amount of facts vastly expanding our knowledge, we are also apprenticed and taught by someone who shows us how to do our work. As a very old symbol of that ancient association with the Guilds and the Barbers, in England at least, we enjoy being termed Mister or Miss rather than Doctor.

I suspect that my mother steered me towards ear surgery so that I might always look after my younger brother who had had a chronic ear infection.

When, decades later, he suffered a brain haemorrhage while on holiday in France, I flew there and took him back to Guy's. My nieces, still students, had to be informed but the most difficult part was telling my parents who were very old, and my mother asked if it was the result of his childhood problems.

I told her It had absolutely nothing to do with it but I think she could not entirely believe me. The anxiety she had suffered so long ago had been rekindled and she felt I had not protected my younger brother after all. I had let her down in the end.

His childhood illness and my mother's plans may have sown the seeds of my career but an intellectual dimension had also built up when, still at medical school, I had become interested in the concept of the soul.

That may, perhaps, be best for priests or poets to explore and I can now no longer revive those early dreams, but in my youthful enthusiasm the mind had seemed the place to start so I attended the psychiatric clinic where one neurotic patient had followed another. I knew it was not for me as they resembled too much one or other of my relatives to be a lifetime's vocation.

I had then opted for neurosurgery, which I soon abandoned, as it seemed to have nothing to do with the soul or even the mind, and was then hardly the neuroscience that might have attracted me today.

The soul, the mind and even consciousness seemed beyond me but I was good with my hands and wanted to be a surgeon, and for those who undertake that exciting if demanding project, it cannot be resisted. ENT surgery might be where I could pursue that great adventure while studying hearing, balance, taste and smell, and as touch was open to all, only vision among the senses would be out of my reach.

My farewell lecture when I left King's College Hospital to become a consultant at Guy's had drawn an unexpectedly large audience, as apart from colleagues and students there were many I did not recognise.

I had called my talk “Windows of the Mind” and I tried to show how, by examining the senses, we could localise intracranial disease, but when I had finished the strangers among the listeners said I had misled them. Psychiatrists from the Maudsley Hospital across the road had come because of my title. My lecture, they insisted, should have been presented as “Windows of the Brain” rather than of the “Mind”.

My defence was that they would not have come and I suggested they explore the mind in the same way, using the senses as windows. I did not mention the soul, which has had to remain part of my youthful pretensions.

In Charge

When working with your hands you are on your own.

When I try to summon up my first day as a Consultant Surgeon at Guy's Hospital my mind turns to the last one instead. I do not know if it is just a trick, as they say, that memory plays, but I feel I have to let such thoughts take their course as some disorder is in the nature of things.

"Which car is yours, sir?" a medical student had asked as I entered the forecourt on my last day, after 30 years, at Guy's. The building on the right now houses offices though it had been wards when first built, its stone facing darkened by the smoke that had poisoned London for centuries, while the one on the left, destroyed by German bombs and rebuilt in identical style, is pristine and pale. Past its double doors there is a McDonald's restaurant, established despite objections, but popular with patients and staff, some of whom had been the protesters.

"Is that it, sir?" the student looked unhappily at my scuffed *Polo*. "Where are the *Rollers* of yesteryear? Where have all the *Bentleys* gone?"

I mumbled something about the handiness of small cars then, realising it was not what he meant. I mentioned the risks of ostentation in today's climate, a form of expression better left to celebrities, but my excuses failed to satisfy him.

"What about us?" he went on. "It would help to see some light at the end of the tunnel. A *Rolls Royce* or two in the Consultants' car park would do little harm or a *Porsche*, perhaps for one of the snazzier surgeons? With all due respect, my younger sister has a *Polo*!"

Maybe I had owed it to them to drive something that boosts morale, if that was what was needed, perhaps crossing London Bridge in a red convertible might have helped them work harder. I had not understood the value of such symbols.

*

No one was in the office on my first day and I noticed that a file prominently displayed on a secretary's desk included my name. The Consultants listed, it said, would be retiring from the National Health Service in the year 2000. The last day of my employment was confirmed on the day it began, perhaps to calculate pension contributions, but I was unnerved by predictions that are best left to providence.

Delighted by promotion I had forgotten that my time at Guy's would be finite, ending with the millennium, which gave it a slightly apocalyptic quality. That event, when it finally came, did so without drama as I did not stop working altogether and let my surgical life peter out gently rather than end abruptly, while Guy's Hospital went on as if nothing out of the ordinary had happened and indeed, nothing had. As we left others came.

*

A large book was by the door, a record started in the 18th century, which members of the staff had signed each day as they came in much as those who clock in to work. This had not been required for a long time but the book lay open as it had for 250 years and anxious to join Hodgkin, Bright and Addison, founders of modern medicine, and Arbuthnot Lane, caricatured by George Bernard Shaw in *The Doctor's Dilemma*, I too signed in until, with so many new wings and entrances, the custom died out and the book itself disappeared. I hope it has been kept as my name is there, together with those who had initiated our scientific era.

My predecessor, a tiny man called Mr Reading, showed me round. I did not know him well as our contact had been limited to the Royal College of Surgeons, he as examiner and I as candidate. He had done all he could to hinder my progress and, obviously embarrassed by my promotion, explained that no one could be right all the time. I shrugged as the least said the better and, after all, it was his job I was about to take over.

He tried to make amends by giving me advice, though only one recommendation stuck in my mind: not to switch off the lights when showing slides during lectures.

"The little buggers creep away in the dark," he said.

Before we parted he remarked that when England's first medical school was founded by Mr Guy centuries ago, the members of the staff would stand at the door collecting a shilling in payment from each student before letting them in.

"They were not so grand then!" he said, perhaps a little vindictively.

I saw him at his farewell party but I did not get to speak to him, surrounded as he was by his protégés and admirers. We had boarded a boat that sailed from Southwark downriver to Greenwich for dinner at the Trafalgar Inn and he threw his head-mirror into the Thames, in a gesture of sorts. Perhaps he had questioned the meaning of his life or maybe he had simply had no more use for it.

*

I was put on a planning committee right away and when I pleaded inexperience a senior colleague brushed my excuses aside. By the time our decisions could be implemented, he had said, I might be near retirement and he and his contemporaries dead. It was our call.

A psychiatrist, also recently appointed, predicted in a rambling speech that there would be no need for mental health beds at all. Care, he said, would be in the community and, though unfamiliar with that concept, I was struck by its originality. The chairman, too, agreed that the future was fascinating.

"But how many beds are we really going to need, Jim?" he enquired.

Care in the community, associated one way or another with cost-cutting, was to become widespread but the psychiatrist with such progressive ideas was offered a lucrative job in Saudi Arabia and did not stay to see it through.

I was curious as to what he could offer them since psychiatry, involving a talking cure, has a cultural underpinning, and I was sorry we lost such an innovative person. I did not blame him for going, buffeted as we were by this wind and that and, for all I knew, care in the community existed in tribal society long before someone had thought of it here.

*

On that first day I had arrived early for my clinic, which was full as doctors come and go slipping into their slot, be it senior or junior, in a relay where the handing over is hardly noticed and the patients are not informed.

"Students over there," the nurse had pointed dismissively.

Could I have looked so young? It had not been easy to persuade her that I was the new chief whose name was on the door and, still not quite convinced, she handed me a starched white coat from the top of a pile.

"Small or Medium?" she asked, looking me up and down, so I pitched into the clinic as if nothing out of the ordinary had happened and continued for the next 30 years when my place was taken, with as little fuss, by my successor whose arrival was also hardly noticed.

I lunched with other doctors in a room offering waitress service, a facility that soon disappeared amid turmoil and hostility. Many felt it was discriminatory to be waited on since it implied servility. Wary of part-time work, the Unions finally put a stop to it so the ladies of Southwark who served us lunch lost their jobs in pursuit of social justice.

The nurses' beautiful dining hall, decorated with Pre-Raphaelite murals, was soon opened to all by the same democratic impulse. Its subsidised food, a relic of efforts to make sure girls ate enough when anorexia was not fully understood, attracted everyone so that too ended and vast self-service canteens were set up to make sure the atmosphere remained egalitarian as that was now the chief concern. It was 1970 and the student revolt set off in Paris in 1968 was still slowly diffusing here and there.

Doctors who lacked the time to stand in a serving queue took to eating sandwiches in their offices while dictating reports, but on my first day the waitress service was still in force and we had a chance to talk to each other.

Maurice Lessof, the Professor of Medicine, gave me a technician and laboratory space, a sort of unsolicited gift offered over lunch, indicating I was welcome at Guy's, while others invited me to live near them in

Dulwich where the schools were good and, though comforted by their neighbourliness, I was used to Hampstead.

Conversation that day had turned to the recently inaugurated London Bridge and I said, somewhat brazenly perhaps for a newcomer, that I thought it had been a missed opportunity and a doctor at the other end of the table took offence. Himself a member of the committee that had picked the design, he insisted it was functional and therein lay the beauty. No excrescences, no bits of nonsense stuck on like fag ends or discarded chewing gum, he said, just simple honest lines. Humbled, I went to have another look before going home in the evening.

A million people were crossing the bridge in the wind and the rain on their way to London Bridge Station, to the trains that would take them home, and in the morning they would trudge back to work in the City. The bridge could have protected its commuters with covered walkways, with arches, which were also beautiful because they were functional for people and not only for cars.

*

A philanthropic city businessman paid a large sum to a well-known firm of management consultants to help us improve throughput in the operating theatres. New and exciting, it bode well for the future especially when a nice young man came asking for our views.

When my turn came to be interviewed he made a note of everything I said. I was convinced that listening to those working in theatres could only be useful especially when the report came bound in blue plastic, though it turned out to be disquieting. Many believed it was to be imposed at once and anxiety was so great that some older members of the staff, both surgical and nursing, announced their retirement.

Theatres, it found, operating like factories that worked 24-hour shifts, would have a much-improved throughput. It ignored the surgeons' other duties, clinics and ward rounds as well as other services such as radiology, pathology and blood transfusion which would presumably also have to remain open for 24 hours.

They explained, of course, that it was a starting point that could be modified and, after many attempts, reasonable proposals emerged. The nurses rejected them anyway as increased throughput was not practical without a vast increase in numbers, and apart from the prohibitive cost there was a growing nursing shortage, a situation which I understand has only got worse even now.

No one mentioned that expensive episode again. We were vaguely embarrassed as no conclusions were drawn and no improvements were made.

*

After working at Guy's for many years there was one major change of which I was unreasonably proud as I brought it about almost single-handedly but more or less unwittingly.

A group of distinguished foreign surgeons had invited themselves to Guy's and amid laughter they told me not to worry as all the surgeons in the world knew that we don't start before nine o'clock in England. I was not amused. I had no idea the whole surgical world knew about this.

I noticed that I was there before eight for a very simple reason. I would never get through the London traffic otherwise. I was aware that my junior doctors seemed to be there too, just hanging around doing this and that until the hospital came to life at nine o'clock so I suggested the foreign surgeons join us at eight in the operating theatres' rest room for coffee and discussion of cases. It turned out many of the nurses joined us as their shifts started before that and were waiting for us a lot of the time.

After our guests had returned to their own countries we continued to come early and waited for permission to start. The rest of the staff, porters, technicians, electricians and everyone else gradually joined us until the Unions, tentatively and discreetly, gave permission and then all the operating rooms seemed to wake up. By half past eight surgery was in full swing at Guy's.

What intrigued me most is that I never met a single person who was unhappy at starting early and everyone in theatres had forgotten that there had ever been a late start.

I remained jealous of the surgeon in Cologne who, when we visited him, not only started at seven with his scrub nurse who was a nun, but also operated on Sunday. My French colleagues were particularly impressed but suggested, "It won't go on forever, you will see!"

It did not go on, of course, the French know about these things. The Cardinal Archbishop withdrew the nurse, the surgeon told me later. She was an excellent scrub nurse, he said, but the Church felt that she had allowed her secular obsession with doing good as a nursing sister to forget her spiritual obligations. I suspect she now prays on Sunday.

*

My welcome at Guy's had been challenging as I had been appointed on the understanding that, without prejudice to anything else I might want to do, it was on the surgery of deafness that I would concentrate, but from the start I was treated as though I was already an expert. Though encouraging, it was worrying that difficult cases had been kept for me and patients told that the new consultant was coming soon.

I was asked to devise an approach to an intra-cranial cyst just beneath the brain by the neurosurgeons who thought it would be more accessible through the ear. I was being painfully careful, taking hours while Omar Shaheen, the cancer surgeon, came to give me support and helped assess the X-rays.

"Lord Brock," the nurse said when I finally finished, "has been waiting to start his case."

The heart surgeon had a reputation for testiness but when I came out ready with apologies I found him having a cup of tea.

"Don't apologise," he said as he sipped, "this is the only place no one can get hold of me and where there is nothing I can do but wait. The only moment I have just to sit and think."

*

I received an unexpected invitation from the Royal College of Surgeons to the Buckston Browne biennial dinner. At first they invited all the Fellows of the College but these were now so numerous that lots had to be drawn and that was how my name had come up.

I hired white tie and tails but I had no decoration while my senior colleagues' chests were plastered with medals. Lack of honours had never mattered but on that occasion I wished I had a couple and I mentioned it to Guy Blackburn, the thyroid surgeon.

"You are lucky," he said. "They are all war medals. I don't wish them on anybody."

We were the hosts, and the guests were to be the Prime Minister and the whole Cabinet. I was surprised that they had all found time to accept our invitation, but when I was told we were supposed to offer them drinks and entertain them first I asked what we were expected to talk about.

"Don't you know?" the President said. "You'll find out soon enough!"

James Callaghan and his Cabinet arrived in a group so I wondered if they had come together by a coach. Is that what governments do? Or do they come in separate cars each with a minder? I followed the other surgeons and offered a glass of champagne to a well-known minister and said something about the weather.

"Er," he replied, "may I just ask you about my gallbladder?"

I said it was not my specialty and took him round to the appropriate specialist who had a little cluster of ministers around him, then a Secretary of State was introduced to me, his wife was losing her hearing and so it went on until dinner, little private consultations taking place all over the great hall in Lincoln's Inn Fields.

The President of the Royal College of Surgeons gave a long, rambling speech pointing frequently to the unappealing painting of Henry VIII who stands arms akimbo, legs wide apart. He is handing the charter to an assembly of surgeons in black robes each about a quarter the size of the king, crouching humbly in supplication.

I lost the thread of what our President was saying, until it dawned on everyone that as he droned on he was actually delivering threats. He said that governments had come and gone but their members had always been sick and would always need surgeons to get them better.

*

Becoming a Consultant meant that I was entitled to have a private practice, see patients outside the National Health Service and charge fees over and above what I was paid for my hospital work at Guy's. My colleague Omar Shaheen suggested that I share his rooms in Harley Street as most private practice was carried out there and in the streets round about. He said I need not pay my share of the rent until I had enough income, which was very kind, although I always managed to pay my way.

We were hoping to make our department at Guy's one of the best ENT departments in the country. When young everything is possible and we even thought, why not *the* best? Why only here? Why not in the world? As good as anywhere in America? That was our aim anyway.

We knew that in order to do that we would have to specialise more and the big division would be between head and neck cancer on the one hand and the microscopic surgery of deafness on the other. We did that with the support of our colleagues at Guy's but faced initial hostility from our specialty in general. That did not last and we did not care, we were on the right side of history.

Omar Shaheen was an outstanding cancer surgeon who quickly set up a joint oncology clinic with the radiotherapists and chemotherapists so that even the thyroid surgeons decided to participate. The work was in such demand that we arranged for our registrar, John Hibbert, to join him after a stint in Liverpool. The quality of their work was very high, encouraging me to do the same with ear surgery with my clinic on deafness in children and pioneering the Cochlear Implant.

Omar held courses in head and neck surgery and many of our registrars, such as Nick Jones who became a consultant in Nottingham, John Watkinson the professor in Birmingham, and Piyush Jani who went to Cambridge, became leading surgeons in that field while Tony Narula did more ear surgery at St Mary's.

Like proud parents we watched them become distinguished surgeons in great cities but I also regretted their departure and would have liked to keep them all at Guy's.

Omar and I held our private clinics at number 97 Harley Street and our secretary from Guy's, Jackie Barnes, asked to join us there when she wanted a change.

*

The patient had "just popped in" as he put it, to thank me and bring a box of chocolates, though I had done nothing. As soon as I had realised he had a cancer of the parotid gland I referred him to Omar who successfully removed it and the facial nerve recovered.

"You did a lot for me," he replied. "You sent me to the best person."

I did the deafness, he did the cancers. In that way we offered the best we could. Were we the best? For a while at least? Maybe, though I suppose it doesn't matter. We spoke on video the day he died. He reminded me we had been to the same school in Cairo, we had worked together at Guy's as well as in Harley Street for 30 years and had been best friends. We said goodbye.

*

Private practice meant a bigger income and I was able to send my sons to a school of my choice at a time when I was uneasy about what was available where we lived. I had to work hard for that.

I also felt that I was part of the exchange system that came when civilisation, perhaps human awareness, first began. I was being paid directly for an item of service.

I was also employed by the National Health Service, enjoying that feeling too and the security it offers. I liked being part of the greatest advance in social security in the history of this country. That no one at all was denied medical care from the cradle to the grave and we could offer everyone the best available in the world. I liked that too.

We don't have to understand our feelings in such historical terms but I was happy to see it that way and I was grateful to have had this opportunity.

Private practice also allowed me to see patients from all over the world which has made my life very interesting.

Deaf Children

I cannot do everything, but I can do something. I must not fail to do the something that I can do. — Helen Keller

"We want you to buy a house for us in Glasgow!"

The absurdity still surprises but the request had come from the Royal National Institute for the Deaf. The system in Scotland also sounded worrying, as I understood that bids are placed in sealed envelopes and the highest is accepted. In fact negotiation takes place between agents who know the value of the property so the procedure was not as mindless as it had seemed.

My role was only representative but I took it seriously and did my best to inspect the premises of what was to be the new home of the old *Institution for the Deaf and Dumb.*

I had spent part of my military service in Glasgow and respected the grandeur of its architecture and the candour of its people though words like '*Deaf and Dumb*' appeared stark, as I too was part of the trend that softens disabilities with kinder labels. When I took over the *Deaf Children's Clinic* at Guy's I had changed its name to *Hearing and Language*, hoping to give it a more positive image.

We replaced descriptions of developmental problems, whether mental or physical, like "Educational Subnormality", by the concept of 'special needs', which points to what we actually have to face — special needs — rather than highlighting a defect. Most of the children who were brought to me did not speak and deafness may have been the cause but it may not, though I was required to deal only with that particular problem. It was difficult to make a diagnosis and if it appeared that the child was not deaf there was little I could do. My predecessor simply turned desperate parents away if the hearing was normal as it was not in his remit, and I imagine that was the reason he had not got on with the developmental paediatricians at the Newcomen Centre to whom I turned.

I looked around the narrow, rundown streets at the back of the hospital trying to find the children's developmental centre where they had invited me to come, saying that they had been expecting my request for some time as they had been told I was a reasonable fellow, for a change. There was nothing remotely like a clinic, much less an institute which already had an international reputation. Among boarded-up rows of abandoned terrace houses, only a derelict pub stood out and in the gloom of the evening and the drizzling rain it was clear I would be late. I turned towards the old Leather Exchange, an area that seemed promising as it was in the process of regeneration, when the creaking of the pub door caught my attention as it swung in the wind. Fastened to it by a drawing pin was a card with a handwritten note saying '*Newcomen Centre*'.

Guided by muffled voices, I climbed the unstable stairs and found a little group of elderly people sitting on low chairs around a children's table in the middle of which stood a bottle of whisky. Dr McKeith, who wore a formal black jacket with a red carnation in his buttonhole, introduced the three ladies as Dorothy Egan, Molly Playfair and Mary Sheridan.

"We were going to start without you," he said, handing me a glass.

Entering a new world, as developmental paediatrics had not existed when I was a student, its fresh concepts made sense immediately though it exposed my inadequacies and inability to manage children with language problems by myself.

We decided that Dr Dorothy Egan would join my *Hearing and Language* clinic on Thursday mornings and I would give a lift home to Dr Mary Sheridan as it was getting late. When I tell people I often drove her home some appear astonished and confess they did not realise she had been a real person as there are many assessment centres, all called *Mary Sheridan Centre*, around the country.

Pamela Snowden, a teacher of the deaf who worked for the Inner London Education Authority, offered to join us on Thursday mornings too. I knew her well and her presence changed the nature of the clinic as we did not have to limit our work to diagnosis, and if a child proved to be deaf Mrs Snowden would take over immediately. This turned out to be of great emotional importance to everybody, ourselves as well as the parents.

For a mother, especially if she had come alone, to learn that her baby is profoundly deaf is so bewildering that most were unable to ask questions or to absorb what we told them, so Pamela Snowden would take them to another room, where the mother often burst into tears. She would arrange to visit them at home and introduce them to the system of education and support which was available.

*

There was a difference between the inhabitants of the adjoining areas of Southwark and Bermondsey. I was told that after the bombing in the Second World War most residents of the borough of Southwark were moved elsewhere leaving behind those of Bermondsey, who were to wait for the second stage of rehousing that was eventually abandoned in favour of restoration. Rows of decrepit Southwark houses behind Guy's Hospital, unoccupied for decades, were gradually invaded by squatters and migrants from other parts of the country, most of whom came as single men and women looking for work, sometimes leaving families behind and forming fragile new relationships. Often frightened and embattled, they lived surrounded by hostile neighbours ready to break into their flat to steal a Hi-Fi or a television, while the people of Bermondsey, established for generations, felt secure among family members and neighbours they knew from school.

Young mothers from Bermondsey came with their own mother and grandmother and often with an old school friend but my heart sank when a single mother from Southwark, sometimes semi-literate, would arrive alone with a disabled child and no one to support her.

Migrants later arrived from other parts of the world, first from European countries like Cyprus, and then from India and Pakistan, presenting a different problem when their children failed to speak. Neither deaf nor delayed in other ways we found nothing wrong with them and so we persuaded Yasmin Saklatwallah, a speech therapist, to join our clinic.

Many doctors and social workers believed that exposure to more than one language confused the child so families had been told to speak only English to their children.

I accepted these ideas like everyone else but I was uneasy as I had been brought up in a multilingual environment.

We had spoken French at home where I had been taught the poetry of Lamartine and Victor Hugo that my mother and grandmother admired. My nanny, already there when I was born, was Slovenian and her delightful Slavic nursery rhymes still sang in my mind, though she spoke to my siblings and I in Italian, a more useful language, at my mother's request. My early years in South America had brought me in contact with Spanish but we then lived in Egypt, and were woken in the morning by the Arabic call from the local minaret. To me languages were just part of a diverse environment, not a threat.

My speech had certainly not been delayed, my mother assured me when I asked. She had taken offence as though I had accused her of negligence but I still thought our bewildering style had better be passed over in silence.

I wanted to find out what balance of languages was the most damaging. Would an excess of the foreign language prove to be the fault? Was it possible that even a slight exposure to Bengali, the language of Rabindranath Tagore and Satyajit Ray spoken, I am told, by more than 230 million people, might interfere with normal development?

I made out a chart, a sort of timetable divided up into morning, afternoon and evening for each day, so that we could mark the hours of exposure to each language. Though unexpected the results should have been obvious as the children who did not speak had simply not been spoken to at all, by anyone, in any language.

Parents worked all day leaving the child with the grandmother, who put it straight to bed when the older children did their homework and everyone was too exhausted to play. They had followed instructions not to confuse the child and forbade the old lady to talk in the only language she knew.

The problem was not confusion or diversity but simply lack of exposure to any language at all.

*

Speech and language delay was not limited to impoverished immigrant workers as we also saw two small brothers who did not speak. The parents were 'in the public eye', as we called it then, though today we would have said they were celebrities, as indeed they still are. I was a little in awe of them and, unsure how to get started, I began by asking how they coped with both a family and their other activities. '*Au pairs*,' they said, were the answer as they had an arrangement with a Scandinavian agency.

"Do you think," asked the father after reflecting for a moment, "that maybe the boys speak Norwegian, perhaps?"

*

Another woman came with her little boy as he was three years old and did not say a word. They were a well-to-do family of what used to be known as "landed gentry" and she was polite but so superior that we came to refer to her as the "Duchess" although her title, we were told, was only "Lady".

We found that the child could hear and did not obviously have any other abnormality. I had no idea what to do next, but the "Duchess" simply took over the consultation as I sat unnerved.

"Perhaps I should hire a speech therapist," she said. "Do you think I should hire a speech therapist? Thank you, that is good advice, that is what I'll do, I will hire a speech therapist!"

She went off talking away, leaving me feeling guilty as I had contributed so little other than to give them another appointment in six months' time. I wondered if you could hire speech therapists to come and live with you in the country? Then I supposed you can hire anyone. You can hire a doctor if you pay enough, I imagined.

I was apprehensive when they did turn up as planned but she burst in with a big smile, handing me a box of chocolates.

"He is cured! He is cured! All thanks to you!" she shouted from the door. "You told me to hire a speech therapist, and I did. He can speak perfectly well now! Tell the doctor you can speak!"

"I can speak perfectly well now, doctor," the little boy said.

The speech therapist had come with them and told me that they lived in grand style in the country with much land, horses and ponies. They sailed, hunted and fished but no one spoke to the boy. All she had had to do was speak to him.

*

Apart from our own better understanding, good came as we visited day care places where many of our child patients were placed and where they were sometimes put to sleep all day with the curtains drawn. Our findings helped change the law and introduce inspections. No one thought they were doing anything wrong including the child-minders themselves.

This gave me a reputation and I was asked to lecture at courses where I pointed out that failure to speak to children was itself a cause of delayed speech development. Multiple languages did no harm and foreign ones were not a disease. I showed off a little by giving myself as an example of someone brought up to speak five.

One group, training to become community physicians, were almost all from the Indian subcontinent and responded well when I insisted that we should never discourage language, any language but I was stopped, as I prepared to leave, by the organiser, a slightly superior woman. I think her name was Dr Robinson.

"I don't want to be rude," she said, "but your accent is not faultless. Is your French perfect?"

My accent, I admitted, though faint and difficult to place, was always in the background whichever language I spoke.

"I thought so!" she said. And walked on, head high.

*

Work with language problems led me to meet remarkable people and follow unexpected paths. One of these was my only involvement with architecture.

The old pub with the creaking door where we saw our patients was known as the Newcomen Centre because of the street, named after a

17th-century philanthropist Elizabeth Newcomen. Widowed and childless, she left a sum for "educating, clothing, apprenticeship and placing out poor children".

Many of these children were trained for domestic service to avoid prostitution and crime but during the last century, domestic service had ceased to be an adequate option for young people, however poor, and Elizabeth Newcomen's establishment was turned into a school of catering until even that could not compete with the food technology colleges and polytechnics.

Dr McKeith persuaded the trustees that today it would be vulnerable children with disabilities that would have triggered Elizabeth Newcomen's charitable instincts, and a new building was planned to house the centre including my own Hearing and Language unit. I found myself on its planning committee and took part for the only time in commissioning a building.

The architects came to show us their design. They wore suits and ties just colourful enough to suggest an element of creativity without frightening anyone, and handed round the drawings of a small nondescript building. It was too banal to be called ugly, and some would have called it functional and therefore having some sort of intrinsic beauty, and though to me banality was a form of ugliness, I did not have the courage to say anything.

"What we do for children with disabilities," Dr McKeith said, "is the best there is anywhere and people come from all over the world to see us at work. Don't you want them to look at your building?"

At the next meeting only one architect turned up, this time with an interesting design.

Eventually my clinic was led by a new generation. Dr Gillian Baird, the developmental paediatrician, took over from Dorothy Egan, who had left us while well in her eighties, and we had recruited an audiological scientist and an educational psychologist. Not a day passed without a visitor from somewhere in the world and I was so impressed by the high standard of what they all offered that I began to question my own contribution in what had become a highly regarded establishment.

I had started by changing the "Deaf Children" to the "Hearing and Language" Clinic and persuaded the developmental paediatricians from the disused pub in Newcomen Street to help me on Thursday mornings. The teacher of the deaf, the speech therapist and the psychologist simply joined us while others such as the social worker just came if she needed to. Some of our visitors, such as Dr Stavros Korres from Athens, had attended every Thursday morning for more than a year and were thought to be members of the staff by the time they left. I never had to raise the salary of anyone as they had all turned up by themselves.

I did overhear one young assistant being shushed to silence when, referring to me, she asked what was that surgeon doing there? That night I tried to find an answer as surgeons should be sent for to do an operation like in ancient times, and I doubt there is a place for them now in a developmental clinic. Children are sent to the surgeons for grommets or cochlear implants but I gathered that the young trainee was told I had founded the clinic, still my clinic every Thursday, and I liked attending so I couldn't be sacked!

My Hearing and Language Clinic has, as the result of its connection with the Newcomen Centre, been copied countless times in many places and lives on. It has also been such an important element in my life. I learned so much about children with disabilities, about parents and families and met so many extraordinary people that I don't think I would have been me had I not been part of it, whether it is now appropriate work for surgeons or not.

*

The biggest role the ENT surgeon has with hearing loss in children is "grommets" for glue ears.

When I was a Registrar at the Royal Free the house surgeon was particularly interested in children who had sticky fluid in their middle ears. She told me that she came from a working-class family in Newcastle with no connection or even respect for education. Selected for a Grammar School place, her parents at first refused and were never supportive. She even "had to go to her Nan's after school to do her homework" as silence or even quiet was not tolerated in her home.

The school doctor referred her to a specialist who gave her a hearing aid. This was then a rectangular beige plastic box worn pinned to the clothes at the front, with a wire leading to an earpiece but her parents would not let her wear it in public. They said she could hear well enough if they shouted so she had to give it to the teacher to keep for use in class. The deafness gradually improved but she could not have done as well as she did without the aid and she wondered if she would now have had grommets.

Moved by her story I imagined her family must finally have been proud of her now that she had become a doctor.

"No," she said. "I am different from them and they don't like it."

That children are prone to accumulate catarrh or "glue" in the ear was noticed as soon as the Zeiss binocular microscope became widely available and school hearing tests brought to light how vast a problem this was. When the "glue" was sucked out through a small incision in the drum the hearing returned at once to normal, only for the glue to form again. Inventive surgeons inserted tiny polythene tubes, about 3 mm long, in the incision. Often they had fallen out by the time the child had left the operating room so we had to become still more inventive.

Someone had shown me that if you held the opening of one of these tubes near the flame of a Bunsen burner, the edges would evert into a circular flange which held the tube in place. Very soon such self-retaining tubes were made in Teflon and sold already sterilised as "grommets" and I did not have to make them anymore.

Visiting surgeons from what are now called "lower or middle income countries" came often to watch the advanced surgery being done by my Consultants but what pleased them most was that when my chief had finished I would show them how to make grommets from fine polythene tubing. They told me that pre-packed grommets were expensive and often unavailable in their countries.

I wondered who the original Dr Grommet might be but no one seemed to know until I had to go to a hardware store.

"You will need grommets for that, shall I get you some?" the shopkeeper said, and I was taken aback when I saw the large flanged objects.

"It looks like a grommet!" I said but he seemed puzzled.

"It *is* a grommet."

*

When I was a Senior Registrar at King's they sent me to watch an Oxford surgeon called Gavin Livingstone operating on children born with no ears.

As it was an extremely rare abnormality, few ENT surgeons had attempted reconstructive surgery and then suddenly, in the late 1950's a spate of babies were born with abnormalities as had never been seen, including some with no ears.

It was soon discovered that this tragedy was associated with a drug called Thalidomide, which had initially been sold over the counter in Germany as a cure for anxiety and tension and particularly for nausea and vomiting in early pregnancy. It was the greatest drug disaster that had ever happened, affecting thousands of babies all over the world.

Gavin Livingstone was attached to a centre which cared for the children that had survived and had taken on the responsibility of operating on those who had failed to develop ears normally.

He was a very kind man and a brilliant intuitive surgeon but not very good at explaining why he did things. He would show me where to start on the bone but was unable to tell me why he chose that particular spot. He seemed to think it was obvious.

He often had to deal with cases where other surgeons had started but given up and sent the patient to him.

"Hah!" he would say. "He was too far back! It's obvious!"

Eventually I, like others, lost heart and decided it was too difficult and that if such cases ever came my way I too would simply send them to him.

Soon after I was appointed Consultant at Guy's Mr Livingstone died, and I received a call from Oxford saying that he had left a dozen patients on his waiting list and as I had been so assiduous in coming to see him operate they felt that I should deal with them.

I had not fully understood his technique but I did not know how to refuse, and my new colleagues at Guy's felt it was my turn now as generations pass on. "If not you," they said, "who?"

I spent much time studying the anatomy of the temporal bone and eventually recognised some more landmarks. I was even able to teach others and, in the 1970's, I suspect most of the cases in this country were sent to me so I did become something of an expert.

I had to face what, to me, was a new experience. Especially the mothers' feelings as they had been prescribed the drug because of their own complaints and though some were bitter at the inadequate precautions of the time, most seem to have blamed themselves for kicking up a fuss. Caring for children with birth deformities and relating to their families was a particularly emotional ordeal and has influenced the way I think even now.

I was invited to give the Gavin Livingstone Memorial Lecture at Oxford but in those early days I spoke very much off the cuff so I had not written out the talk and I have lost it now.

*

I was so attached to my Hearing and Language clinic that I rarely questioned my role in it. I had created it after all and had to make a decision about it only once.

It was always understood that intracranial problems were the realm of neurosurgeons and the ENT specialists willingly kept away. The nearest we got were mastoid abscesses that had extended inside the skull and could best be drained from the ear where they had originated.

ENT surgeons were always interested in the facial nerve because it was sometimes damaged by infection or surgery of the ear or parotid gland, and paralysis of the face is a particularly ugly deformity. Nevertheless tumours of that nerve which usually appear in the bony channel between the ear and the inside of the skull were traditionally left to the neurosurgeon. Except for Dr Bill House in California, that is.

Bill House, like all ear surgeons, had gained considerable expertise with surgery under the microscope and suggested that he try to dissect the facial nerve away from the tumour before the neurosurgeon removed it, avoiding paralysis. This proved so successful that I had gone to watch him operate and later I went to learn from Ugo Fisch in Zurich. I carried out a few such operations which I found technically very interesting but each one took me many hours before I handed over to the neurosurgeon. There was also a certain *cachet* attached to what became known as "skull base surgery" and I wished to become part of that select and revered group of ENT surgeons.

On holiday in La Jolla, near San Diego, I received a telephone call from Bill House to invite me to visit him in Los Angeles. I was flattered that he had taken the trouble to find me through my secretary in London and I joined him right away.

He suggested I join the House Clinic, a great compliment no doubt, but I had no intention of leaving Guy's. I realised that I could not take on base of skull surgery with its long hours without dropping my children's clinic. I thought a lot about it and worked out that by the time we might be able to offer an alternative to Fisch's department in Zurich or the House Clinic, I would be nearing retirement age and would have to pass on this work anyway.

My solution was to offer that possibility to our registrar, Michael Gleeson, who showed great ability and, in time, it worked out very well.

Looking back I have had no regrets about that.

Research

Creativity is intelligence having fun. — Albert Einstein

Although I had been invited to apply for the Consultant job at Guy's, when the committee asked what my plans were I did not think they really meant it. No one had come from outside the department since the first ear surgeon, a writer and social philosopher called James Hinton, first set it up a century ago so I felt my chances were so poor that I might as well suggest my own fantasy unit. The cost would have been unacceptable, I imagined, as the clinical side would be accompanied by a research group including technicians, a research assistant and scientists. To my surprise they agreed to everything and supported me ever since.

*

I suppose that some justice was done when Luigi Galvani was reinstated as Professor Emeritus even though it was after his death in 1798.

A visit to the Anatomy School in Bologna was how I learned that curious fact and yet, from one thing to another, from one coincidence to the next, it was to inspire my research and affect the rest of my life.

They say it was also chance that made Galvani famous. While dissecting a frog in 1786 its leg, touched by an instrument that had picked up static electricity, kicked out as if it were alive. He studied the phenomenon which he called *bioelectricity*.

Experimental science had been taught in Bologna as 'Natural Magic', a name which might still, perhaps, be appropriate. Galvani had led the usual life, marrying Lucia Galeazzi, another professor's daughter and a woman said to have been well liked as well as a scientist in her own right though, according to the conventions of the time, she was not formally credited for her participation in Luigi's work. He lectured and wrote until an honourable retirement but things took a turn for the worse when he refused to swear allegiance to Napoleon's Cisalpine Republic and his pension was withdrawn.

The Emperor had obviously not been impressed by bioelectricity but soon after his defeat at Waterloo, Mary Shelley took a copy of Galvani's book to read on a trip to Lake Geneva. The notion of using electricity to bring dead tissue to life led to the story of *Frankenstein* and I too returned from my Italian holiday with an intriguing idea.

Nelson Kiang, an American scientist, had shown how a sharp sound sets off electrical discharges in muscles, which is not surprising as animals tense up for fight or flight when alarmed by even a faint sound, but my own idea had come from seeing a dog pricking up its ears on Hampstead Heath. The sound had been so quiet that I could not hear it and I wondered whether the muscles behind our own ears, weak vestiges from primitive ancestors, generated electrical impulses even though they failed to produce a twitch.

To study this phenomenon a physicist called Keith Humphries was assigned to me. Reticent and somewhat inarticulate, he wanted to enclose the room in a Faraday Cage, a mesh designed to protect electronic equipment from external interference, but the cost was considerable and I insisted he find another way.

He simply disappeared but I was relieved when Keith reappeared a few days later with the equipment wrapped in metal foil bought at Woolworth's for two pounds. When I showed a colleague from New York round my department he scratched around the walls looking for the Faraday Cage and was furious when I showed him what Keith had done as they had spent thousands to isolate his laboratory.

I am told that shoplifters used that technique to avoid detectors.

I took on a young registrar, Bill Gibson, to assist me, and our small team saw results almost at once. My real job, of course, was to get on with clinics, operations and waiting lists and research was viewed as an indulgence despite what had been expected of me. Early success, however, was both encouraging for me and made my work acceptable to those less sure.

I recorded electrical responses to sounds from the vestigial muscles behind both ears and called our system the 'Crossed Acoustic Response' or CAR, and finally the moment came to test it on a newly born. Hearing, now routinely tested at birth using one electronic device or another, is hardly noticed, but it had never been done before.

The senior midwife refused to let us into the maternity ward on the grounds that Keith looked scruffy. The obstetricians, tuned to her changing moods, were unwilling to press her, but eventually we compromised and she agreed that babies going home on the day of their birth would pass by our laboratory on their way out.

The first mother kept looking at her watch while I explained the procedure.

"Will this take long?" she asked.

When responses to clicking sounds appeared on the monitor I could not resist a flourish.

"Madam," I said, "your baby's hearing is perfectly normal."

"Thank you," she said. "Can I go now?"

"But this is the first time," I insisted, as I just could not let go, "the first time in the whole history of the world, of humanity, that someone's hearing has been tested at birth and we have a bottle of champagne in the fridge!"

She had more important things to do and, of course, her baby was fine so we drank to the moment by ourselves.

*

Tomorrow's World, from BBC television, did a program on us. They were very good and I came to admire the presenter, Judith Hann, for her intelligence and thoughtfulness. I used my cousin's baby daughter, now the writer Tanya Sassoon, as my subject and the program, widely watched, led to a large pile of letters which I put aside to savour the satisfaction of reading when I had more time.

None contained praise, much less support. All were hostile and some abusive.

I tried to classify the letters hoping it would help me understand them better if I kept the findings in a scientific manner and, sensing that their place was not with my technical papers, I took them to read at home.

Some doctors wrote that electrical tests were unnecessary as they recognised deaf children perfectly well using just skill and experience. Others insisted that assessment of the whole child mattered more than just the hearing. I began to reply that the CAR was just an extra tool which did not prevent anyone from using their talents or training, but as I read on I realised that the letters expressed the common anxiety that skills on which their livelihood, their self-respect even, depends no longer have any value. Some parents of deaf children wrote to urge that I cure deafness rather than expose it and I stopped answering the letters. Not one offered encouragement for the work I was doing. I suppose they did not think I need any as, after all, I was on television.

Consequences are not predictable and when I was recently admitted to hospital for special tests, one of the consultants was very excited. He had seen the *Tomorrow's World* program when he was aged nine and it had helped him decide to become a doctor.

*

The Central Office of Information also came to make a film intended for the outside world, and I thought it would go smoothly as we were now used to the camera but the director appeared uneasy.

"Do we have to have that nurse?" he asked.

"She is our nurse," I replied. "She always places the electrodes on the baby's head."

"Personally I don't give a damn," he said with some irritation. "In fact I am Irish myself but we are supposed to show off British science to the rest of the world. British doctors, British nurses."

I must have appeared confused as he shrugged impatiently.

"Can't we have an English nurse?" he said. "Does it have to be the one from Jamaica?"

I said she was our nurse.

*

The British Association of Neurologists invited me to their conference in Liverpool, and I was intrigued by a suggestion from the Professor at the Institute of Neurology in Queen Square.

He had found that electrical responses to visual stimuli were slower in patients with multiple sclerosis, and noticed that the few cases of multiple sclerosis among the slides I had shown implied the same effect to sound.

I had been unaware of these effects though I had been puzzled by the delays which we had labeled *prolonged latencies*, but now it made sense and we could confirm a diagnosis of multiple sclerosis by seeing how long it took for the muscles behind the ear to respond to a series of clicks.

I told my neighbour about this while we gardened, talking over the hedge. He asked me to test his wife as she was convinced she had multiple sclerosis, but I refused.

Supposing it proved positive? My observations did not cure anyone and I did not see the point of depressing someone who had only had one episode and may not have another attack for many years, if ever.

As it turned out she did not have multiple sclerosis but the marriage did not last. I was glad I had not got involved.

The Crossed Acoustic Response took me to unexpected places.

*

On one of those early London nights, slightly misty, the sun must have disappeared by four or perhaps already fading away by three, only one man was still waiting.

He said he was not a patient but he wished to consult me about something else.

"I watched you testing a baby's hearing on television," he said.

"At birth!" I stressed, rather pleased. "The first time in the history of the world. The day he was born we knew he could hear!"

"Does that mean that you can tell if someone hears, whether they cooperate or not?"

It turned out that the man was a Lloyd's underwriter with a bizarre story to tell.

A Sicilian peasant of limited means was severely injured while in Rome and on regaining consciousness was found to have lost the power of speech altogether as well as his memory, and had been left with other severe neurological disorders such as inability to walk.

He had recently taken out an insurance with Lloyd's of London for a million pounds so he was brought here, hospitalised for investigation and when his condition was confirmed his claim was paid out in full.

Not long after, another Sicilian who was also visiting Rome slipped on the Spanish Steps and was knocked out. An ambulance took him to the Gemelli Hospital where he regained consciousness complaining he could not hear, and it was noted that there was dried blood in both ear canals. Nothing was found on examination and the X-rays were normal but numerous audiometric tests showed he was totally deaf. He made a claim to the same insurer who, becoming suspicious, followed the man and saw him sitting in a park chatting with the first claimant.

This was clearly a case that could easily be resolved by the CAR test and I was delighted to examine the claimant who came to Guy's with a tall, thin man who said he was a Professor of Legal Medicine in Rome. Everything went wrong, however, when the Professor and his interpreter discovered that I could speak Italian and understood their conversation. When my machine started clicking away they pulled off the electrodes and left, saying they had not agreed to such newfangled unrecognised technology.

That was only the start of the saga, as it was agreed I should go to Milan where we would reproduce the test at the Maggiore Hospital in Dr Lenzi's clinic. As clicks began the claimant pulled off the electrodes again and ran out into the street with me calling out rather foolishly, "*Aspeta! Aspeta!* Wait!"

I could not catch him as he disappeared amid the traffic of the Milanese afternoon.

The Lloyd's underwriters told me they had all they needed, paid me a small fee for having saved them money and I was glad to have another use for my test. I was unable to remain in touch with Dr Lenzi who never answered my letters, which I regretted as I liked him.

I thought that was the end of that story as indeed it was for many years, until one day I saw Dr Lenzi again at a conference in Madrid. I waved politely but he sought me out and said he had always wanted to give me an explanation for what had happened.

After I left Milan he had a visitor. An elderly, well-dressed man had come to his clinic. He wore a fur coat, his hat was a vintage *Borsalino* and he carried a malacca walking stick with a silver pommel.

"We know," the man had told Dr Lenzi, "where your daughter Michaela and your son Paolo go to school. We just want you to stop having anything to do with Lloyd's and stop any contact with that English Professor. That's all we require to leave you and your family alone."

Curing Deafness

Every one of us is blind and deaf until our eyes are opened to our fellowmen, until our ears hear the voice of humanity. — Helen Keller

Sound is our business.

Our world, gas, solids, liquids, the bones of our skull, the air we breathe, consists of particles and if they are made to vibrate at a rate between 20 and 20,000 oscillations every second special organs deep in our ears can sense them and transform them into electrical impulses which travel along a nerve to the brain. This is the audible range which we can hear.

Broadly speaking there are two types of deafness. The first is called "Conductive" in the English-speaking world though in France, with good reason, they call it "Of Transmission". Here the nerve of hearing functions normally, conveying electrical impulses from the special sensory organ, the cochlea, in the inner ear to the brain where we become aware of and recognise them as speech, music or noise.

In conductive deafness it is the transmission of audible vibrations across the outer and middle ear which does not function properly. The eardrum may have been perforated or scarred by infection, the chain of little bones, also known as ossicles, that act as levers to amplify the vibrations may have been damaged, interrupted or stiffened up.

These transmission problems are often the result of infection but can also be inherited and may even be present at birth. In fact all sorts of things may happen to these ossicles which are also known as the hammer, the anvil and the stirrup because of their shape, not their function, and if the sound vibrations are not transmitted properly from the eardrum to the cochlea conductive deafness is the result.

Nothing much could be done about it until the Zeiss operating microscope became available after World War II and a German, Professor Wüllstein of Würtzburg, used it to operate on the damaged ossicles in an attempt to repair them.

It was essentially to cure conductive deafness that they wanted me on the staff of Guy's Hospital. It could only be done by relatively young surgeons as the older ones had not yet developed the skills and eye-finger coordination required for microscopic surgery. I had started my career as a witness to what happens when new technology is introduced as no one could do it at the Whittington, so they had failed even to buy the Zeiss microscope though the money had been made available.

It showed how useless it is to throw money at projects when it is the right people that you need. I, still in my 20's, had taken easily to microsurgery.

I remembered that not long ago when I had an argument with a leading scientist who said that she was horrified by the time spent by children on computer games. I think I made her cross when I said that it trained the surgeons of tomorrow by improving their eye-finger coordination.

*

As far as I was concerned the surgery of deafness, the microscopic surgery of the little ossicles of the middle ear, had started with an American surgeon from Syracuse in New York State called Sam Rosen. I was naturally in awe of the founder of our specialty and it was almost a shock to stand immediately behind him in a dining room queue at a London conference. I introduced myself with trepidation, but he pointed out that as we had both missed the bus for the official reception we might as well dine together.

The surgery of otosclerosis is where I had started and practised so assiduously and Dr Sam Rosen was happy to tell me how it had all begun. It was, he said, "chance favouring the prepared mind".

He had devised an incision to enter the ear which we called "Rosen's Incision". Today there is a tendency to dismiss the name of any individual so we refer to it as an "endomeatal incision".

He told me that while he was operating on a deaf patient for something unrelated to the hearing, his hand had slipped. His heart stopped, he said, when he felt a slight but quite definite crack and he withdrew his instrument instantly asking the patient, who was awake under local anaesthesia, whether she was alright. The patient, amazed and delighted, announced that she could suddenly hear everything. The operation, though initially carried out by a chance prod in the right place, spread like wildfire as, with the binocular microscope, the surgeon could now see what he was doing and that led to further advances.

Rosen himself was embattled when he told me his story as there seems to have been a political side to it too. He had actively supported the socialist Henry Wallace for president against Harry S. Truman and sheltered the radical black singer Paul Robeson in his own home at the height of McCarthyism. Rosen could cure deafness so his ostracism had been only social, but it still rankled.

A young surgeon from Memphis, Tennessee called John Shea Jr went a step further by replacing the fixed stirrup or "stapes" ossicle with a plastic piston.

This operation was called "stapedectomy". It cured the conductive type of deafness due to otosclerosis and taught surgeons to use the operating microscope as well as helping to introduce "spare part surgery".

I also met John Shea Jr at a conference in Cambridge when we stayed in the same college and had breakfast together. I was impressed by how young he looked and had achieved so much already. He seemed hardly older than I was and immediately told me that he was earning a million dollars a year. I did not know what to say as I was a junior registrar at the Royal Free Hospital then and the NHS did not pay us much. I am sure he meant it kindly, as encouragement perhaps, though I never achieved anything like that. I don't think anyone ever did in England. His reputation among the juniors was no doubt enhanced as he had also married Miss America 1960. From our point of view he had it all.

*

I was a teenager when I first read about Helen Keller and I experienced a sense of panic, like being buried alive, when I tried to imagine being both deaf and blind. I had closed my eyes in the silence and I thought death must be better. At that age, of course, we have a different concept of mortality and death has not got the same finality.

It was years before I could face reading what she wrote, and I did so only because patients with this double disability had come my way. I was amazed at the rich content of what she had to say, and I realised that it was blindness and deafness of the mind that prevents engagement with the world.

"Blindness cuts you off from things; deafness cuts you off from people," she had said.

Dealing, one way or another, with hearing impairment in both adults and children has been the essence of my work but the way people respond to deafness has often surprised me.

*

I became attached to an extraordinarily good-looking and charming couple.

The wife, fair and striking like a Pre-Raphaelite angel, seemed to hold herself at a distance, a stance attractive in a beautiful young woman unable to hear what is going on around her. Severely deaf, she had been the victim of what we called 'botched surgery' and the surgeon who was to blame had brought her to me, divesting himself of the responsibility by assuring them that I did nothing other than repairs. It was simply the way things went with surgery, he had said, where there were specialists for everything so she would be fine now. I was hardly confident and explained that it would be a gruelling and risky enterprise as she would require at least three operations, each with the risk of total deafness and screaming tinnitus.

I became convinced that we were successful in the end only because of the devotion of her husband, a youthful Adonis with blond hair that shone like a halo, so that the arrival of these beautiful people invariably caused a hush in the outpatients. Always by her side, he interpreted for her as she could read only his lips.

It had taken great courage to submit to such risky procedures though she finally emerged with normal hearing and as surgeons sometimes do with their successes, I had become so attached to the couple that I missed their visits when these were no longer necessary. They were an example of how much can be overcome with the support of a loyal partner and I took it as an important lesson.

She returned alone for review a year later and, no longer distant in bearing, she chatted pleasantly to the nurses. When I asked after her husband I was stunned at her reply.

"I got rid of him," she said.

"Why, why?" I asked. "He was such a nice fellow."

"But what a bore," she shrugged, then brightened up. "I have a new man now! Thanks to you, entirely thanks to you, I didn't need James anymore."

She explained how, trapped by her inability to communicate, she had become so dependent that she had felt like her husband's prisoner.

*

A particular group of deaf women had avoided both surgery and hearing aids. Each had come alone with hardly anything to say and refused, sometimes angrily, any treatment, leaving hurriedly as they averted their eyes. I could not understand why they had bothered to come but then each of them returned within days, often accompanied by a married daughter.

"She wants the operation!" the daughter would say.

This happened often enough for me to recognise a pattern. I never saw the husbands and the post-operative visit was also predictable as they came alone and I could see grim, unhappy faces in the waiting room. Fearing that the operation had not been successful, I soon found that although they had done well they were not pleased, and whatever change hearing had made to their lives not everyone felt it was for the better.

A very elderly couple provided a clue. The husband, who was aged 85, did all the talking, as the wife who smiled pleasantly was so deaf that it was not possible to carry out a conversation. They knew she could be cured by surgery and left smiling and nodding when I arranged a date and returned grateful and delighted by the successful outcome.

They seemed so pleased that I asked them why they had not come before. The wife told me that they had had such a happy, though childless, life bound up in each other, excluding everyone else, that they had not wanted to change anything. She had been content living entirely through him, and he was relieved to be her only interpreter.

They had changed their minds at the end of their lives, he explained, only because he had suffered a severe heart attack and they did not want her to be left alone unable to communicate.

*

My dream unit had come into being and I found myself at the head of a group that was involved in the most advanced hearing research. At the same time I was part of the Newcomen which was well ahead of any child development centre in the world, and the adult clinics and surgery we offered was as good as that available anywhere. Visitors came from all over, young surgeons from Seattle and Johns Hopkins Medical School in America came for a year to Guy's as part of their training and each day I worked with colleagues I greatly admired.

It is, however, only as I look back that I see how fortunate I have been. All those years I think I was just happy with my lot and did not look for a reason.

Then Larry Hench got in touch with me. He had been given my name by an anaesthetist he and his wife had met on a boat trip in the Canary Islands and who told him she was certain I would be interested in his work.

A Professor of Material Science at the University of Florida in Gainsville, he had been developing materials that could replace the ossicles that transmitted sound in the middle ear.

This could sometimes be done with plastics such as Teflon, but there was a problem where it had to bond with the other tissues such as the eardrum as inert materials were extruded and fell out of the ear.

It was disappointing for the patient and mortifying for the surgeon when that happened. One of my registrars handed me a Teflon piston, a tiny thing, that a patient said he had scratched out of his ear.

The story illustrates the embarrassment ear surgeons felt as a result of material rejection and the number of repeat operations we had to do. We did not know what to call these procedures as after three or four "revisions" colleagues asked if we ever got things right first time.

We began to call them "Stage II" or "Stage III", which seemed positive rather than incompetent as our operating lists were pinned up at the Royal College of Surgeons in case visiting doctors might wish to attend, and I asked Professor Portmann, a French colleague, what they called these embarrassingly repeated efforts.

He looked astonished, as the French do when faced with what they believe is a problem only to the British.

"*Retouche*, of course!" he said. "Like when an artist touches up his painting just before an exhibition."

I thought only the French could pull that off.

A Belgian surgeon called Jean Marquet pioneered the use of eardrums and ossicles taken from cadavers and, excited by that new approach which had been quickly named "transplant surgery" and "body parts", I had got to know him well and had been one of the first to apply his technique which quickly became standard procedure. The problem appeared to have been solved as there was no rejection and transplants of all organs, catching the public's imagination, had become generally popular. The King of Belgium made him a Baron, rather sadly as he was on his deathbed by that time.

Progress is rarely straightforward and a friend told me of a peculiar finding she was about to publish. A small number of people who had been given hormones extracted from human cadaver glands had developed a fatal illness called Creutzfeldt-Jakob Disease or CJD. Mad Cow Disease, of which it is a variant, had not yet appeared and AIDS was still unknown but it seemed to me that a solution other than body parts was necessary, so I fashioned grafts from the patient's own tissues instead which was also not without problems.

*

That was when Larry Hench arrived from Florida with his wife, June, herself a scientist.

He had created a glass that had the remarkable property of bonding with tissues as well as bone so it would not be rejected, when no such material had been available before. I began to work with the Henches and a bioglass replacement ossicle was soon available. Known as the *Douek Middle Ear Device*, it is the only object to carry my name or to have reached the market and that is thanks to my American colleagues rather than to any entrepreneurial skills of mine.

It also got me attention of a sort when the writer Victoria Glendinning wrote a novel called *Flight.* The story has nothing to do with me and the hero, alas, is certainly not me, but it has to do with glass and she referred to my work and to me by name. I think she was slightly uneasy when she mentioned it in case I was not happy, but I was delighted.

To have my name in a novel was splendid even if only as a brief allusion. It occurred to me that had the doctor called in to treat Elizabeth Bennett's sister, Jane, in *Pride and Prejudice* been a real one his name would have survived over the centuries. There are many others such as the one who tends Marianne Dashwood in *Sense and Sensibility* as well as the numerous soulful doctors in Chekhov plays, and now I too was in a novel.

*

Fascination with the eardrum's appearance when I had first had access to the operating microscope had led me to a strange observation when I was still in training at the Royal Free. A young woman complained that her hearing felt muffled, although I could find nothing wrong. Her eardrum looked even better than normal if that is possible as it shone, reflecting light like a mirror. I could not resist stroking it gently with an instrument whereupon it cracked, the surface fragmenting like a windscreen that has been struck by a small stone. I was horrified at what I saw and asked if she was all right.

"Wonderful," she replied, "thank you, I can hear much better now!"

It had been the *bouffant* hairstyle, fashionable at the time, that was to blame. Girls backcombed the hair and kept it in place by spraying liberally with a lacquer that solidified instantly. If it got into the ear it formed the transparent shining layer on the drum which had misled me and which I was able to peel off. Spirit ear drops dissolved it away.

Fashions changed and I never saw this problem again but experience is handy and decades later, my own registrars were puzzled by an elderly actress whose muffled hearing was put down to age as she was over 80.

Her thin straggly hair, each curl stiffly hiding a bald patch, took me back and I asked if she sprayed it.

"They do it at the studios," she replied. "They spend hours sticking every strand where they want it."

I recognised the highly reflective surface of her eardrum after so many decades.

Unusual, unexpected reactions always come to mind, of course, but operating on the middle ear allowed me to cure deafness in many people and although I also had to overcome the dismay of failure, which all surgeons have to learn to handle, the successes were numerous and gave me great satisfaction.

But that was "conductive" deafness. If the deafness was of the second type which we had been taught to call "perceptive" deafness and changed to "neuro-sensory" or "sensori-neural" (I could never decide which one I preferred), we only had a hearing aid at our disposal. These had vastly improved, but for those who had no hearing at all to amplify there was nothing that surgery could offer. Some teachers saw it as an educational opportunity which I was to discover only later and to my cost.

*

Early on a Saturday morning I received a telephone call asking, or perhaps ordering me, to come to the Department of Health and Social Security. Although polite, the call had made me uneasy as, waking me up, it played into my anxiety dream.

I had not mentioned that dream to anyone until I discovered it is quite common. I dreamt that there has been some sort of misunderstanding, a mistake in the record only uncovered after all these years, that I have not passed my exams after all, so I am not qualified, not really a doctor. I invoke squatter's rights to my good name and my job of senior surgeon and teacher of London University, but I am always faced by diffident bureaucrats who, though open to compromise, are uncertain how to handle such a situation which, they claim, has never happened before. The officials suggest that the simplest way of getting rid of the problem is for me to take all the exams again and though the dream lacks the terrifying urgency of a nightmare, I wake up in dismay. The last time it came I had remained aware that I was now retired and that my career, my life in fact, could not be taken away after it had already been lived. That was to be my final argument and although anxiety is still around it is no longer expressed as having to retake examinations.

I made my way to the vast government building at the Elephant & Castle with some apprehension and had to wait downstairs until an overweight middle-aged woman with a limp asked me to follow her along endless corridors as she slowly hobbled in obvious pain despite leaning heavily on a stick.

"My hip," she explained, stopping to catch her breath.

I apologised for her trouble and said I could have found my own way.

"No, no," she said, resting again for a moment. "People get lost or fed up wandering about the corridors and don't turn up at all. I think they go home."

She threw open a door into a large room where people were sitting or standing around.

"The Undersecretary of State!" she announced with a sort of flourish, gesturing towards a man sitting at a table, and added, after regaining her breath, "for Health."

The man immediately complained that there had been no progress in curing deafness as though it was my fault and, although taken aback, I replied mentioning the new operations we were doing.

"That is for conductive deafness," he said triumphantly, delighted that he knew the difference. "But what about nerve deafness? What progress there?"

Reassured that I was not being held personally responsible but was only representing my specialty, I answered back.

"And what about cancer then?" I asked. "Why have they not cured that?"

It turned out that the Secretary of State, a feisty red-haired Labour MP called Barbara Castle whom I had actually met and admired during a youthful, if brief, moment of political interest, had promised a deaf fellow Member called Jack Ashley that she would make sure he was cured when she came to office. I felt I was being encouraged or bullied into fixing nerve deafness and that is how powerful people work. They order someone to do it.

I saw it as my chance and explained that it would be rather costly. The undersecretary said I should apply to the Medical Research Council, promising that the Minister would signal her support for whatever I came up with.

Walking down Borough High Street back towards Guy's Hospital searching for ideas, it was memories instead that came to mind.

Dr Howard House, reporting from Los Angeles on behalf of his brother Bill, had enlivened the first conference I attended as a registrar by showing a film of a deaf girl with an implanted electrode in her ear. Responding to electrical impulses, she appeared to recognise nursery rhymes, and there was much applause and praise at this breakthrough presented as the first time someone with nerve deafness had heard anything.

Behind his back many in the audience sniggered. Familiar rhymes could be recognised just by tapping the rhythm, they said, while I, hoping to ingratiate myself, ran up to Dr House to tell him about the Vietnamese patient I had seen so many years before in Paris.

I was 17, I remember, and toying with the idea of becoming a painter or, on the other hand, perhaps a writer. Why not both?

My mother had other ideas for me. She had brought my younger brother to Paris for a major ear operation which was done by *Professeur* Maspétiol, the Chief at the St Antoine Hospital. It was a repair exercise after surgery in Egypt and she suggested I talk to him about studying medicine.

Vague, then, about what to do, I was reasonably interested, and the Professor exuded an infectious enthusiasm for his specialty which may possibly have decided the course of my life. He took me to a ward where a girl from Vietnam sat with her head swathed in bandages and I saw that a wire peeped out connected to a microphone into which he spoke.

"*Allo, allo tu m'entend?*" he said, while the girl nodded and smiled with pleasure saying, "Ah! Ah!" every time he spoke.

Maspétiol, too, was delighted and explained that the patient was totally deaf with no cochlear function at all and was now responding to electrical impulses which she perceived as sounds. She was the second patient to have had a cochlear implant. The first one ever had been done by his colleague Charles Eyriès but that critical advance in the history of medicine had resulted in a quarrel with the physicist, André Djourno, and Maspétiol had had to take over.

I can't say that any of this meant much to me and I never found out what became of the girl but it must have had an impact on me as I tried to tell my story to Dr House, though he had seemed annoyed rather than interested.

He pretended not to hear at first but when with awkward lack of insight I kept insisting, he mumbled something about experimental work done by the French. Americans at the time often avoided mentioning that they copied other peoples' work, especially from a distant country, but I had pressed on, trying to please, until he managed to get away from me.

These memories all suggested ideas to me and a patient, deaf on one side, helped me compare what he heard when his dead ear was stimulated electrically with real sounds in his good ear.

The reception was cool when I submitted my proposal to the committee. Not meaning to be unkind, the scientists meeting at the Medical Research Council made it clear that they considered me someone whose skills would be valued if surgery was required but who could hardly be expected to understand the complexity of sound vibrations, their translation into electrical impulses or their perception and interpretation by the brain. I felt foolish as the chairman gently proposed that another scientist, expert in phonetics, could be asked to explain why my proposal was nonsense though he did not use such words.

I thought I would not bother to come if I was simply going to look a fool, but I was intrigued when I learnt that the professor in question was the successor, a few times removed, of Professor Higgins, who taught Eliza Doolittle to "speak proper" in *My Fair Lady*. The man on whom Shaw had based his play, *Pygmalion*. As it turned out Adrian Fourcin was one of the exceptional people who were to help me expand my knowledge and my life in many ways.

As Gabor's student he had entered his laboratory after the Nobel Laureate's funeral to be faced by the ghostly image of his mentor sitting in a chair. Though our work had nothing to do with holograms the thought of an ethereal replica surviving in perpetuity made me wonder whether memorials of the future will be holograms rather than marble statues, especially in cultures that venerate ancestors or change their minds about heroes.

To everyone's surprise Adrian Fourcin had concluded that my project was actually a good idea. Our partnership went on to the end of my work in research and I gained enormously from his friendship.

Our endeavour was vast and demanded more skills than the two of us could provide and attracted assistants who soon turned into friends. Experts in sound perception, processing, electron microscopy and specialties I had never even heard of began to join my team.

I presented our early results at the Royal Society of Medicine to a standing ovation and the press was already talking of a Bionic Ear. Those were exhilarating times as I stood where the action was and doing all I had ever wanted to do. At that moment I felt that my dream had come true as I had not had to lower my sights or accept that my hopes had been a waste of time.

We took on a PhD student, John Walliker, who had an innovative mind and whose ideas pointed us in directions that were unexpected and exciting. Guided mainly by scientific curiosity, neither Fourcin nor I were capable of interrupting research to concentrate on a device that could sell in open markets. Though it did not seem so at the time, our search for perfection, or even improvement, contained a flaw as far as commercial success was concerned.

On the other hand we contributed much as we were in constant and close contact with other researchers in California, Paris, Austria and Australia. We travelled from Melbourne to Los Angeles, Boston and San Francisco, taught a course in Beijing and I was a Visiting Professor at John Hopkins in Baltimore. Paris was near and both Fourcin and I spoke French so we worked closely with the successors of the team that first introduced the concept of electrical impulses that could replace sound perception. Indeed, the Paris team was at St Antoine and they introduced me to Eyriès, the originator of it all and now a very old man. For me a circle was closed.

There was no doubt that people who had no hearing whatsoever could now, with the implantation of a device which transformed sound into electrical impulses, hear something. By no means perfectly, but something.

The Department of Health was not finished with me either, as bureaucracy too does not sleep. I had ceased to feel awed by them and this time the telephone call had come during a clinic, so busy that people were waiting in the corridor.

*

The official must have sensed my annoyance and quickly said that he had read about my work with the Bionic Ear in the papers that day and wanted to congratulate me as, he insisted, some of his best friends were deaf. He was concerned only by the cost.

I explained that there was no cost to the NHS as the cochlear implant program was entirely funded by the Medical Research Council.

"That's just it," he said. "We don't want another disaster like the kidney business. That started as research and now all this dialysis and transplantation cost millions!"

"True," I said, "it would be cheaper if they all died."

I now regret my sarcasm as, though he might have chosen his words better, there is a case to be made for costing and his job was to do the books for us since that was not for me.

*

All was clear then until everything became equivocal and open to debate and life turned into a series of unexpected consequences.

I arrived at the station in Manchester with Bill House, the American surgeon who, ignoring the French, was still acting as though the cochlear implant was his creation and I was not prepared to argue. We walked, as the hall where we were due to speak was not far, and we must have presented an odd pair as he towered over me and every now and again he placed a hand on my shoulder as though I were a stick.

A small crowd surrounded the Princess Theatre, a demonstration as the police were there, and we could see placards and banners, but it was only when we got near that we could read what they said.

"DOUEK AND HOUSE LEAVE THE DEAF ALONE"

I was confused but Dr House said he often got this in America and told me to pay no attention.

We were at a world conference of teachers of the deaf and after I had spoken, a congenitally deaf man with no speech sent up a note which was read out by the Chair, Winifred Tumim, herself the mother of two deaf girls.

"Tell Mr Douek that in sign language the deaf have a culture of their own and that what he is doing to the deaf community is cultural genocide."

I had no answer and attempted to avoid a reply by mumbling something about it being a comment rather than a question and everyone being entitled to their views, but Mrs Tumim insisted that I address it.

I said it was the right of parents and grandparents to want to speak to their baby and it was not for the deaf community to take the baby away as though it was a new recruit to a sect of their own.

I sounded reticent and do not think that, perplexed by the complexity of these concerns, I was very effective. Hostility continued when we went on to Paris for another meeting.

Those working to help the deaf to hear had come from many countries and were invited to a concert in Notre Dame. It was stopped by a group of congenitally deaf people blowing painfully piercing whistles which they themselves could not hear.

Shaken, my wife and I walked out into the street taking the *Rue de l'Abbé de l'Épée* across the Seine and, when I remembered that it was that same, theologically dodgy and unlicensed *abbé*, who had founded the first school to use sign language in 1760, well before the Revolution, I looked for the original site at 14 *Rue des Moulins*, near the *Palais Royal*.

With much to think about we kept on walking, taking the *Boulevard Malsherbes* as far as the *Boulevard Péreire* as that had been named after the Péreire brothers, great entrepreneurs who had established the railways in France and the grandsons of Jacob Rodrigues Pereira, a Jewish refugee from the Inquisition who had introduced the method to teach deaf people to speak.

Gill and I walked for half the night along streets named after individuals now hardly remembered so that I could think about the perplexing opposition to the work I had been so proud of. Evening in Paris lends itself to walking as well as reflection.

What became clear to me that night was the outsider status of the two men who had done more than anyone else for deaf people. The priest who, because of his dissenting views, had been allowed to teach them only because his deaf pupils were not expected to grasp his dangerous ideas and Péreire, the Jewish refugee, who was also to give France a family that would be at the forefront of its industrialisation. Spain and Portugal, the two countries that had been desperate to be rid of dissent and diversity, sank irreversibly into stagnation that has lasted till now.

*

By chance I turned on the television on my return to England only to see myself smiling benignly while describing the anatomy of the ear. It was an old clip as I looked younger and then the camera turned to a man who spat out his words with venom.

"Consultants," he said, referring to me, "like that one, believe that because the deaf cannot speak, they have no emotion!"

I wrote to complain that what I thought was exactly the opposite of what I was being accused of, but when I eventually received a reply the television company simply said that there had been no time to enlarge on my views and that the presenter was only illustrating a point by using me as a sort of prop.

Few people saw that program so I suppose it did not matter, and some even claimed I should be happy simply to appear on television and what was said about me was neither here nor there. I cannot keep reassuring myself that nothing matters or my whole life might fall into that category.

*

The story of Cochlear Implantation has not yet reached its conclusion.

We were dealing with ears that simply failed to respond to sound. If there was even a slight sensitivity to vibrations we could try a hearing aid, so it was the last challenge in our attempts to cure deafness.

There was also a dramatic difference between those of our patients who became deaf after they had developed speech and those who, born deaf, grew up never having heard speech at all and therefore never learnt to speak adequately.

As surgeons and researchers determined to cure disabilities we found ourselves in a world riven by controversy. The debate had gone on for more than 300 years and the dispute is hardly resolved even now. It took me a long time to understand all its implications.

Congenitally deaf people had spontaneously developed a language based on gesture, manual signals and facial expression. Later, with the help of dedicated teachers anxious to improve communication between deaf and hearing people, sign language was organised into a valid language with its own cultural identity.

But there were other teachers who tried, using their own techniques, to get people to speak, however inadequately and it was in the middle of this dispute that we found ourselves.

I was trying to offer some hearing where there was none, and excited by the scientific advances we were making I assumed everyone would be pleased. When it became clear that we were intruding in a longstanding and deep-seated controversy I was simply shocked and uncertain how to respond.

The man had said that what we were doing was "cultural genocide" and I understood that what he meant was that if we finally cured deafness and all children who were born deaf could now learn to speak, a whole rich culture based on sign language would die out which, I suppose, was true. I still went on advancing the science where I could.

*

Our group, which I had named the "Guy's Hearing Research Group", included a postdoctoral electron microscopist and biologist, Hilary Dodson, who was based at Guy's and who later married John Walliker. We worked in close association with Adrian Fourcin and his department at University College London, and with Brian Moore who soon became a professor in Cambridge. These were all people I both liked and admired and who provided, throughout my time as a surgeon at Guy's, the intellectual balance I craved.

Although we contributed in various ways to the development of the cochlear implant and have been referred to as pioneers of the "Bionic Ear", we lacked the entrepreneurial, as opposed to the scientific, skills which could have taken us forward commercially. I have always felt that it should have been, perhaps, my role and in a sense I failed to endow Britain with a homemade cochlear implant. On the other hand I am not nationalistically inclined so I don't really mind which company made one in the end but no British enterprise, as far as I know, had shown much interest.

In the end I watched Australian and other companies move into making the implants with the knowledge gained from all our combined research. The Bionic Ear was here and there was a general sense that we had achieved our great aim in virtually curing both types of deafness. I expressed a slight feeling of disappointment that we now had to step aside and leave it to the manufacturing engineers to provide us with devices and my French colleague, Claude-Henri Chouard, who was sitting by my side admitted that he felt the same. He thought for a moment and then said: "*Mais on s'est bien marré, quand même*!"

It is one of these French expressions that cannot be totally translated but it means, more or less, that we also had a lot of fun. He retired, I am told, to an island just off the coast of France where no cars are allowed and where he can paint in the sun.

*

Sometimes, discoveries come unexpectedly but we can only take them beyond interesting speculation if we have the team already set up to follow our ideas and test them.

I was summoned to the maternity ward and I went with apprehension as I was usually called when a baby was born with a malformation. Cleft palates and absent ears left parents bewildered and in tears, asking when everything would be put right, hoping something could be done at once.

This time a midwife was waiting and insisted I put my ear to an incubator to say whether it was working properly.

"I am not an engineer," I said. "I know nothing about machines."

Someone had told her I was in charge of sound when, short of incubators, they had rented them by the hour from an agency. She had put her ear to it and called me not knowing I was only the surgeon. When I listened I too was shocked that small babies were placed in such a noisy environment and decided to investigate.

The noise level was just below that known to damage ears so it was not recognised as a problem. Yet, one out of every 14 premature babies had some degree of hearing loss and the causes suggested were no more than guesswork. Despite the reassuring measurements I could not believe that the noise in the incubator was acceptable and arranged for an experiment that exposed newly born guinea pigs together with their mothers in the incubator noise.

Immature ears proved more vulnerable than those of adults and I wondered how much more susceptible those of the premature must be. It seemed the noise could, after all, be responsible for much of the hearing loss in preterm babies and we reported this to the *British Medical Journal* and the Department of Health who alerted the manufacturers.

The *Journal* rejected our paper and sent me a copy of the peer review. It was scathing and urged the editor to suppress our contribution as it would lead to unnecessary anxiety among the parents, industrial disruption and offence to those who ran the units. We were, they claimed, accusing these outstanding people of deafening babies. The editor added a word of his own on the telephone, expressing disappointment that work coming from such a prestigious institution as Guy's could be of such poor quality.

I had never received such a mortifying rebuff and wanted to drop the whole matter so I called my team together and passed round the letter, not having the heart to read it out loud.

I asked them, one by one, where we could have gone wrong. Hilary, who had been responsible for the electron microscopy, in tears, assured me that she had repeated the experiment many times and her findings could not be faulted and, getting the same response from everyone else, I decided to go to another journal. Before I lost courage I went, the same day, without an appointment to see the editor of the *Lancet.*

I handed him the letter from the *British Medical Journal*, the disparaging anonymous review and lastly our paper. He read through it all without a word as I sat by his desk.

"I will take another paper out of the next issue," he said, "and print yours instead next week!"

"Are you sure?" I said. "What if they are right and it is rubbish?"

"They can write and object," he replied. "We will publish that too!"

He called me back as I reached the door.

"My daughter is expecting a baby," he said, "and when my grandchild is born I don't want it put in a noisy incubator, whether you are right or not."

Changes were immediately introduced by the manufacturers and the national press reported our findings widely. Gregory Bock, who later was to run the CIBA foundation in London, working in Montpelier confirmed our findings, which were also used as evidence in American courts. Cases of deafness in premature babies dropped and we went on to study the side effects of drugs that were made worse by noise.

There was not a word from those who had tried to prevent the publication of our work. They would not talk about it after they dropped their anonymity and I still do not understand what led them to do what they did. They must have thought they were doing the right thing.

Almost 30 years later I received a letter from a French doctor. He thought I should know that there had been a sudden rise in deafness among premature infants in his area following a reorganisation of services that had introduced helicopters to take babies to a regional centre in Bordeaux. No one had checked that they were protected from the noise of the engines.

I think that perhaps I might have done more good with that piece of work than with any other as we saved the increasing number of babies placed in incubators from being deafened. Preventing deafness is better than curing it.

Singers and Performers

I don't know what happens to me on stage. Something else seems to take over.
— Maria Callas

Some see themselves as out of the ordinary because they feel that way, but occasionally a few really are special and, however irritating they might be occasionally, we enjoy what they offer.

My first experience with a singer was a young man who had been admitted to the Whittington for investigation but nothing serious was found so my chief had lost interest.

I had never met a singer and my only experience of performers had been a ballet dancer called Julie whom I had taken out when I was a student, impressed by her link with the arts which, I imagined, would raise our relationship into a higher sensibility. Sweet as she looked and ethereal when she danced, all she and her friends could talk about was their feet. Feet, backache, joint pains, jobs and auditions. Singers are similar, and relate to their voice as if it were almost extracorporeal, an instrument to be maintained and honed, a gift to the world which everyone must wish to preserve. Some become stars and their practical and emotional needs encourage those around them to turn into courtiers, often undertaking menial tasks such as fetching the star's children from school or entertaining their elderly parents, so that everyone feels they have a role in the production of each masterpiece.

Singers and actors can be so difficult to handle and occasionally exasperating that we should avoid them altogether as patients unless we enjoy their performance enough to take them on. We cannot expect stolid, emotionless persons to express delicate sentiments. These people have to make us weep and we should be prepared to look after them and their needs.

There is also mystery. I watched the Italian conductor, Claudio Abbado, explaining a story of intrigue and unrequited love to Pavarotti, the famous tenor who quickly interrupted him.

"Just tell me," he said, "move to the right, to the left or whatever you want me to do and let me sing."

Though seemingly uninterested or unaware of the deeper meaning of the story his voice moved us to tears.

"How do you explain that?" the conductor asked me.

All that was in the future however, long after I was left, as usual, to deal with the young singer at the Whittington Hospital.

He explained to me he was a *helden* tenor, a rare voice that although often described as a high baritone is, if properly trained, one that deserves a place in its own right; large, rich and textured.

He had had no symptoms but on a chance examination his right vocal cord was seen to be paralysed. His voice had been unaffected as the other cord compensated for the immobility of its fellow.

The singer was reassured and the abnormality was put down to a virus as that is acceptable to most, but he had become hysterical. What was going to happen to his prized *helden* tenor voice? He wept, running back and forth to telephone Lucy Manein, his teacher.

The singer's anxiety had involved me in the concerns of baritones, tenors and singing teachers.

"Maybe you were born like that," I suggested to him on an impulse. "Maybe that is what makes you a *helden* tenor rather than an ordinary tenor."

Instantly, he was a different man, cured and happy. He telephoned to let me know that Lucy Manein had remembered that Richard Tauber, famous in the 1920's and 30's, had also had a paralysed vocal cord. My patient was so grateful that he would contact the Tauber family for more information to help my career.

That family sent a solicitor's letter threatening to sue, with an affidavit from a very elderly Czech doctor, who still lived in Hamilton Terrace, denying that Tauber's exceptional voice was due to a paralysed cord and that, until he was dying of cancer, his vocal cords moved normally. His voice was the result of an intrinsic superiority and not of a physical abnormality.

I cannot remember how it ended or what became of the singer in my relief at escaping litigation. I have looked after many singers since but I have kept my distance, though it meant that I have had to forgo the glamour of circulating among celebrities and have usually gone straight home after the opera.

Decades later I went to Vienna as an emergency to examine Luciano Pavarotti at short notice. I was puzzled as to why they wanted me since there are enough specialists clustered around the Vienna Opera, but I agreed to go as I admired the singer.

The star travelled by private jet with an entourage of many people and the chauffeur had gone before to drive straight to the plane where customs and security did their checks on board. I was booked into the Imperial, the same hotel as the tenor, and waited downstairs for him. Nearby a man was listening to a walkie-talkie.

"They have left the room," the metallic voice said. "They are making for the elevator. Tell the car to approach the door so he walks straight into it!"

I joined the retinue but faced new problems, as the Viennese professor was furious that I had been brought in as a second opinion, and in order to pacify him I said it was an honour to visit his clinic. His ego seemed as frail as that of his patients but this appeared to reassure him.

"Do you see many famous patients?" he asked when he saw me admiring the signed photographs of singers and film stars on the walls.

"I head a large teaching department, perhaps the largest in England," I confessed, "and I have to see what comes."

"Even people from the street?" he asked, amazed.

"Especially those from the street," I said, but we were now on friendly terms as he had ceased to feel threatened.

A tiny camera down the nose of the patient makes it possible to see the vocal cords in action on a monitor and that was what had caused the crisis. The Professor had noticed a tiny protrusion near the tenor's cords and raised the alarm. When I asked what the problem was the singer said his voice was fine so I suggested he show us.

"What shall I sing?" he asked.

All I could think of was the duet from *Lucia* and, in that small examination room, the magnificent voice was so powerful that it hurt my ears but there was nothing wrong with it. The professor agreed but remained puzzled by the feature he had noticed, and he now seemed grateful that I was there to share the responsibility.

"Maybe," I said, remembering the young *helden* tenor so many years before, "maybe he was born like that, maybe that is the reason why he sings like he does."

All was resolved, everyone was pleased and we praised and congratulated each other. The tenor invited me to supper as they let him cook a pasta for his entourage at the Imperial Hotel, and I think he was disappointed when I had to decline and asked for the loan of his car to take me to the airport.

"Does he really cook at the Imperial?" I asked the driver.

"Yes," he replied, "he makes a good spaghetti but we all have to stay and eat so as not to upset him. Some of us would rather go out on the town but he does not appreciate that and thinks he is doing us a favour."

*

Another tenor with a sore throat was due to sing at Covent Garden the following night. He was ill with a high temperature and I wrote out a certificate for the insurance, which seemed straightforward had I not felt unexpected pressures from his entourage who crept in as soon as I had finished my examination.

The conductor's contract depended on that particular tenor because if he did not perform the conductor had the right to cancel, but he chose to carry on so another cause for anxiety was that the singer who replaced my patient got rave reviews.

A member of the coterie had tried to make me sign the singer off for two weeks instead of one, which I thought unnecessary. I was puzzled but the conductor, who was a friend, explained the reason to me later. That tenor, at the peak of his career, was due to star in *Lohengrin* in Vienna but his team feared that the pinnacle is also the beginning of decline and that a Wagner opera might expose the aging process just a bit sooner than was necessary. Apparently critics listen like hawks for the earliest signs of faltering as it triggers a cut in the fees and therefore in the income his managers, agents and sundry employees can expect.

Performing celebrities risk being ruthlessly pushed off their pedestal and have been booed by spectators who have asked for their money back. This causes enormous anxiety among the dependents and generates fears of letting people down as well as of rejection. I have often been aware of these emotions and felt sorry for aging idols facing the vindictiveness of those who create heroes in the first place. I am not sure why it seemed that tenors and sopranos were the most uneasy, but perhaps I was wrong.

Recalling these memories has made me realise how often I had misunderstood what was going on beneath the surface of these people's lives.

*

I did see the third tenor too. It was a Sunday morning and my wife and I were already in the car for our weekend away but I went in. Gill did not begrudge him as singers get so anxious, as he is a decent man and as he sings so beautifully that we want to keep him going.

In the end I have seen all three tenors.

*

I was asked one evening while finishing my clinic to visit Michael Jackson at the Dorchester Hotel where he was staying before a huge concert at Wembley.

My first reaction was to refuse, as the agent had called during a busy clinic at Guy's where each patient was important to me, and I was annoyed at the effect on the nurses who had been so excited by his name that they had no qualms at interrupting me. However, I also felt I should have no pretension of deciding who was deserving and who was not, and I was intrigued so I suggested he came along right away and wait.

Michael Jackson was, the manager explained, followed by photographers and reporters camped outside the Dorchester, and a trip to Guy's meant instant headlines. Attempts to escape in a laundry van or in disguise had been foiled by bribed hotel staff, so I agreed to go.

I was greeted by bodyguards who saw me through one door after the other until I reached the star who was sitting in a corner by himself reading a magazine. The manager said he was reading about himself and I asked him who wrote all that.

"We do," he said.

I could find nothing wrong with him so I reassured him and said there was no reason why he should not give a marvellous performance which I was looking forward to watching on television.

"Say goodbye to Mr Douek!" the manager told him.

"Goodbye Mr Douek," the star said, and I asked the manager how old that sweet, childlike performer was. He said he was 39.

The *Evening Standard*'s headlines announced the following day that he had left for America, as a specialist had warned that if he sang he might develop nodules on his vocal cords. The insurance must have paid out a huge sum for the cancellation at Wembley Stadium.

I had said nothing of the kind so I called the manager as well as colleagues in America. I felt somehow responsible, though I was not sure about what, and found out that he had left for the airport immediately after seeing me and it was his doctor in Los Angeles who had given him a certificate. He had said that he could *develop* nodules if he sang, which is always a theoretical possibility. I was curious at what sort of fees these accommodating doctors charge but I never found out.

*

I liked the performers. Some were nice, some were not so nice, like everyone else, but I was never particularly friendly with any of them. I can only recall one rock star who was actually discourteous and kept me waiting only not to turn up at all. But I have no idea what was behind that diva-like behaviour so for all I know it may not have been his fault.

Despite assumptions to the contrary I found a sort of humility and reasonableness in virtually all these celebrities and the only ones to whom this did not always apply were a few insecure singers.

What amused me most about actors was how unlike they were to the characters they portrayed. My favourite occasion was when my secretary, Jackie, arranged for me to see an actor I had only recently watched playing

Winston Churchill. He had done this so well that it inspired in me what I had felt as a child during the war when we looked to Churchill literally to protect our lives.

When I actually met him he was obviously no Winston Churchill in real life. A rather petulant little actor who performed well.

Sometimes I even got angry on my patients' behalf. There was one well-known and wonderful actress who was treated incredibly badly by a director. I got so angry that I rang him up to tell him to lay off if he did not want to wreck her performance altogether. When I asked her how old he was she said he was her younger son's age.

*

I had my own moment of standing on the stage to applause, but only one.

Gill and I went to the music festival in Pesaro one year but all the arrangements had been made by friends, who also collected us from the airport in Bologna. There had been some delay so we were barely on time and were ushered in as the conductor was about to raise his baton. The trouble was that we had come in by the door at the front of the stage in full view of both audience and orchestra. As we tried to tiptoe in, the conductor stepped down and, grabbing me by the arm, dragged me onto the stage. I was naturally embarrassed as it felt as if I was going to be admonished for coming late in front of everyone but then I recognised the conductor, Alberto Zedda.

"Ladies and gentlemen," he said, "this man has saved my life!"

I mumbled something about his hearing, not his life but he said:

"He who saves a musician's hearing saves his life."

The audience applauded and I was allowed to find my seat.

Zedda had been injured in a road traffic accident and lost the hearing in one ear as the little ossicles that transmit the sound vibrations in the ear had been disrupted so, in theory at least, it was possible to replace them by an operation. There were many risks, however, as the surgery was very tricky and the hearing could be lost forever.

A number of Italian surgeons had the skills to do this but they had preferred to send him abroad.

Zedda had told me that he was well known there and none of the local surgeons wanted to risk being labelled the man who had deafened Alberto Zedda, whereas if my hand slipped few here would care.

For whatever reason I too had my moment of glory.

*

During our research work on the cochlea I was given a laryngograph by Adrian Fourcin, a device he had invented which allowed us to analyse the wave forms produced by the opening and closing of the vocal cords as they could be directly transformed into the electrical impulses we used as a stimulus to the auditory nerve.

The waveform provided us also with a physical interpretation of pathological voice conditions. We could study, for instance, the regularity, asymmetry and stiffness of the vocal cords and although most of the registrars who followed the head and neck aspect of our department were mainly concerned with cancer I was able to inspire a few into studying the voice and one, Julian McGlashan, went on to specialise in the voice.

When we appointed the first female ENT consultant at Guy's, Elfy Chevretton, I also tried to interest her in the voice and was pleased that she has developed a specialised clinic including therapists, microsurgery of the vocal cords and a specialist registrar. I was pleased because it showed that Omar Shaheen's and my vision had succeeded and we had left behind us a great and diverse department.

I was left with one regret regarding the voice as I had had another idea for voice research which I never got round to. I have always felt a little guilty about it as I had planned to do it on retirement, but I also feel that our system could have made greater use of retired surgeons by encouraging them to stay in some capacity. I would have liked that.

My idea was simple: to record the voices of all patients attending the neurology clinic using a laryngograph and analysing the result using advanced digital techniques.

Obviously I cannot anticipate what the result might be but some of my questions would be whether we can diagnose or predict the onset of motor disorders like Parkinson's from changes in the voice pattern. Can we record a deterioration, predict its evolution or gauge the effect of drugs?

Maybe someone will be interested.

Kings, Emperors, Dictators and the Like

Man will never be free until the last king is strangled with the entrails of the last priest. — Denis Diderot

If you work in London as long as I have you meet all sorts, and that is how I got invited to Vanessa's wedding.

Unlike some doctors I was not often invited to patients' social occasions, but Vanessa's parents were particularly grateful to me and insisted so much that I accepted, and as it turned out to be a resplendent occasion they must have wanted to give me a treat. The guests were very grand and, indeed, the Queen herself was there and though I was never anywhere near, I could watch her eating from a distance as we ate our own dinner at the reception. Can I say that I had dinner with the Queen? Technically, I suppose I could.

I had been relieved to see that the GP was there too so I could chat with her and her husband, a cardiologist. The GP also knew some of the other people sitting at our table and introduced me. I do not remember all of them as it happened a while ago but I was pleased to talk with the dressmakers who had made the bridal gown and the hairdresser I had recognised from the newspapers.

"Do you think we are at the service table?" the GP whispered in my ear.

*

Constantine, known as Con, was my audiologist at Guy's. A Greek Cypriot from Bethnal Green who, despite a balding, portly Mediterranean bearing, spoke with East London inflections, he reassured the patients with warmth and empathy, drawing out their concerns, which he passed on to me. He was particularly kind to immigrants whose English were poor and those who found it difficult talking to doctors.

Few things are worse than the blank look from a doctor who has yet to read the referral letter or forgotten who you are. Con's personal approach helped me counter impersonality.

At a Royal visit to the hospital I had been instructed not to speak spontaneously but to shake the proffered hand and introduce the members of my department as the party moved along.

"Get him away!" the Vice-Chancellor had whispered as Con went on chatting amiably with the Royal visitor, his expressive hands occasionally touching the visitor's shoulder in a friendly manner. When Con took out a piece of paper to write out his telephone number the Vice-Chancellor insisted I intervene.

"Their older relatives have trouble with their hearing aids," Con explained, "so I said they can give me a call anytime. Anytime at all."

Years later when Con had been in charge of the audiology department at Guy's for some years, singular events were taking place which many of us failed to understand fully. It had been decided that Guy's would amalgamate with St Thomas' and King's. This arrangement, known as GKT, or Guy's, King's and St Thomas', has now been in place for so long that hardly anyone working in these establishments remembers when they were separate entities, so it appears to everyone to be in the nature of things. At the time it thwarted the intense loyalties on which these charitable hospitals had relied for centuries as well as caused professional anxiety regarding promotion or even loss of employment, and other units felt threatened by Con's position. An attempt was made to get rid of him and he had to defend himself before a packed and hostile committee. The usual suspicions of the day were rumoured against him including misogyny, racism, all nonsense in his case and Con lined up with great pride his most distinguished patients as witnesses on his behalf. These included a former Lord Chief Justice, a peer of the realm and other well-known persons, and then it was whispered to me that his opponents had altered their tactics and that a sort of elitism was exactly what would be held against him. I called instead on the poorest, most vulnerable and deprived patients to whom he had been kind and his position was then unassailable. Con's career was unchallenged till his retirement but I had become wary of the culture that was around us and it prepared me to face the world that has emerged.

*

We did not do well with Royalty at Guy's with few, if any, Honours or Knighthoods, and our Senior Physician was blamed as he had been appointed a Royal doctor. His grounds for resigning were obscured by rumour but I was told it had something to do with being sent for without good reason in the middle of the night. No one, I understood, had resigned from such a post before though some had been dismissed and one had even been hanged, drawn and quartered on suspicion of espionage, but that was in medieval times and the Lord Chamberlain had agreed to our doctor's request, so Royal work did not come our way.

*

My secretary, Jackie Barnes, had said that Frank, the general surgeon, wanted me to see his patient right away and not wait till tomorrow. If a colleague calls you, you go, so I went straight to the private clinic but he hadn't told her the man's name.

"You've come to see Frank's patient?" the nurse on the 5th floor had said. "The poor little Emperor is very scared!"

After examining him with difficulty it was obvious that there was nothing for me to add to his management nor was it realistic to reassure him about his condition.

I was often called to patients for whom nothing could be done as anxiety can be transferred from what actually matters to inconsequential symptoms such as a tickle in the throat. It is a way of side-stepping reality.

He dismissed my words with a wave and, grabbing me by the lapels, pulled me towards him. He asked if I had watched his interview on television and wanted me to know that the clerics who were running his country were not what we thought.

"You think these ayatollahs are like the Church of England, called in to calm the spirits?" he whispered hoarsely. "You'll see what they're like!"

I could still hear him desperately calling out as I reached the door. "You'll see what they're like! You'll see!"

*

The Dean of their medical faculty had come all the way to London to invite me. I was not keen to go as the Middle East was said to be unstable, but when people say they need you it is difficult to refuse. Perhaps it appeals to our original calling, the obligation to respond when you are sent for or perhaps it is flattering to just be wanted.

My arrival was greeted with unusual pomp and as it had been arranged for me to demonstrate some surgery, when the moment came to operate I was attended by a large group of doctors. After discussing the X-rays I scrubbed up and went towards the anaesthetised patient, only to find that the doctors had all disappeared.

I told the nurse to call them but she pretended not to understand, and the anaesthetist eventually asked me to start without them. As I had come all the way for this demonstration I was not sure what to do, but I insisted that I needed an assistant at least to hold the retractor.

The most junior of the doctors appeared, a man called Riad with a big moustache that stuck out beyond his mask. He cowered in a corner and I had to coax him into coming nearer, foolishly imagining that he was overawed by assisting the surgeon from London.

When I had finished I found the little crowd of doctors clustered outside the theatre doors and, unsure as to what had happened, I apologised, believing it was somehow my fault that they had missed the operation, but they kept offering me tea.

"Have some tea!" they all insisted as though they had been told that if the British get agitated, tea will calm them down.

The following morning it became clearer when, always surrounded by my escort of doctors, I went to see the patient who was sitting up in bed and offered me chocolates. The ward was like an armed camp with guards brandishing automatic weapons contrasting strangely with the profusion of flowers.

The patient's face, free from tubes and tape, now looked familiar but I asked the doctors who he was. They replied at a tangent as they said he was very grateful and when I insisted they simply repeated that he had told them to thank me.

Eventually they gave a collective explanation.

"Our Party," one said, "is like Labour and Conservative joined together."

"And Liberal!" someone else added.

I said, rather pompously, that I was familiar with the structure of the one-party state and demanded to be told who my patient was and after whispering among themselves someone finally spoke.

"He is our leader."

"And we love him very much!" they added quickly all together.

I was occupied with teaching and visiting the country until the patient had recovered sufficiently for me to go home. People came to tell me about his cruelty and I heard he had invited political leaders to his office, locked the door and shot them himself. An orthopaedic surgeon who had been placed in the sun in a corrugated iron coffin for a week also came to tell me his story and there was an atmosphere of fear that I have never experienced elsewhere.

When I saw the dictator for his final consultation he asked if his headaches would cease. I pointed out that headaches can have many causes and suggested that a man in his position must often be under stress. He looked at me coldly and said he also had the sensation that plotters were around him and wondered if that was normal.

The interpreter looked as though he was having a heart attack; his skin was grey with sweat around the lips when I asked if it was possible that they were really scheming.

"We plotted against my predecessor," he said flatly, "and we killed him."

At the end of my stay I was asked if I wanted any money.

I was not sure what to say as I just wanted to go home but I was bundled rudely into a car as though I was a prisoner, which I suppose was their way, and taken to the National Bank, a large open plan building where a tiny angry man wearing a green visor, like in 1930's films of American poolrooms and gangsters, was waiting.

I said I had changed my mind and in any case their currency was useless to me but that seemed to agitate him even more and he said I could have as many dollars as I wanted.

"Can I have pounds?" I asked.

"Anything," he replied. "Swiss francs, Deutschmarks, whatever you like."

I could not resist pushing it out of curiosity.

"Swedish kroner?" I asked.

"I have those too."

He took me to a huge safe opened by a circular door that responded to what looked like a steering wheel, and inside were shelves stacked with currencies.

"How much?" he asked.

I was taken off balance but the fee for such an operation in London at that time was £700 so I asked for double, explaining I had come a long way, though he showed no interest.

"Is that all you want?" he insisted in a tone of contempt. "Fourteen hundred pounds? That's all?"

I suppose I could have said I meant ten times that, fourteen thousand or who knows what but, both mortified and frightened, I slipped the money into my pocket and left quickly.

In London, the Inland Revenue asked if I was sure that was all they had paid me. One of them raised his eyes to heaven and I think he believed me when, maybe because of his pitying expression, I was reminded of Clive of India who had been made to account for his wealth before the House of Lords. The Maharajah had, he explained, taken him to his treasure house, itself a palace with mountains of rubies and diamonds, rivers of sapphires and emeralds and told him to take what he wanted.

"I stand astonished," Lord Clive had said, "at my own moderation."

I was not in that class.

*

I was invited to Warsaw.

Poland under communist rule was subservient to the Soviet Union (which meant Russia). The local dictator or sub-dictator, a drab individual called Gierek whose only aim was to keep things under control, was widely despised though he tried to give the impression that he was secretly covering for his citizens.

Rubbed out from the map over the centuries, Poland feared the alternative was to disappear again, merging into the Soviet Union like Ukraine, another part of the old Czarist empire and the Baltic States.

They had given me a chauffeur and a white van that I assumed was from the hospital but which I later learned belonged to a state company making dishwashers, and that the chief executive was a hypochondriac who had a fear of cancer.

"We see him whenever he feels anxious," the doctors told me, "and in return we get dishwashers. He lent us the van when we promised you would examine him when you came. You will find that there is nothing wrong with him but we got the driver and van in return."

Barter between skills and power emerges when money is not significant. My Polish colleagues also told me about something they called "internal exile". It meant a standoff with the Communist Party, which left them alone if they kept away from politics and renounced professional advancement.

"He is in internal exile," they would state blandly when I found a highly respected surgeon in an inferior post.

My hosts had made arrangements to take me to the Opera but were apologetic as *Tosca* was playing and they would have preferred something from Eastern Europe, Janacek perhaps.

There was something unusual about their *Tosca* which I did not quite figure out until I realised that although it was entirely traditional and sung in Italian which I understood, the gestures and facial expressions of the performers suggested that the villain, the police chiefcalled Scarpia, was a decent chap at heart and even a fellow victim of the protagonists. I knew that opera well and I was amazed, having never seen such a thing.

"Scarpia looks over his shoulder," the Professor of Surgery explained, "at Big Brother, the Soviet Union. After Czechoslovakia everybody is afraid the Russian tanks come here next, and Edward Gierek protects us in his way so we must not hold him responsible for despotism."

Back at the dismal Hotel Europa I found an Australian woman who had been on my plane, here to sell Aussie films, looking shaken.

"I need a couple of drinks," she said. "They took me to see Harold Pinter. In Polish."

I told her about the opera.

"They made Scarpia the star!" she said. "The bloody police was the hero!"

The traditional villain, the police chief, was made to seem heroic although the music was the same, the lyrics were the usual ones, but the way Scarpia kept looking over his shoulder did the trick.

"Bloody Scarpia!" the Australian called out as she was being helped away. "The poor bugger had fallen in love with Tosca! He was offering to protect the idiot dissidents from good old Big Brother!"

That was long ago and a young Polish medical student seemed only politely interested when I told her about my visit to Warsaw. She could not remember communism, she said, but her parents had told her about it.

*

A daughter of the King of Arabia was admitted to a London hospital struggling for breath. I could hear the desperate choking sounds as I entered the Intensive Care Unit.

I was then told that the King had to be consulted before any surgery but they had not been able to get hold of him. The duty officer at the Foreign Office had nothing to recommend but sensibly suggested I do what is right.

"A tracheostomy or she will die," I said to the anaesthetist who had been waiting for me. "What time is it in Arabia anyway? The King will be asleep."

After she had regained her colour and the breathing had settled they had finally got through. The King had said we should do whatever was best.

She remained a problem as she was uncontrollable and had taken her retinue to the West End at ten o'clock at night as soon as she was able to breathe through a tube in her neck. The ward sister threatened to resign if she continued to be ignored.

"They let her in the shops at any time," the nurse who had gone with her said. "She buys tons of stuff."

I ordered the window to be opened despite the cold and the rain that blew in.

"She is not a prisoner," I said. "She can go whenever she wants and wherever she wants. She can also throw herself out of the window if she wishes. No one must stop her, the window is open, and she can even jump now."

Tantrums over, the princess was contrite and I was weary.

Later, when she was ready to return to Arabia, I dropped in to see her on the way from my clinic at Guy's where the mother of a chronically ill child insisted I give her a letter for the Housing Authority. Mould grew on the walls of their flat in a housing estate in Lambeth and made her son wheeze. She thought my letter would get them rehoused, though I was doubtful.

"A doctor's letter!" she said. "Of course they will listen."

When I got there the Princess was waiting to go. Arab patients never mind being kept waiting, however exalted their status, perhaps theirs is a culture where time is not what matters.

She said that they lived in a very inconvenient palace in Riyadh and wanted me to give her a letter so that, in view of her health problems, the King would allocate her a more suitable one. When I wondered if he would pay any attention to what I said she seemed outraged.

"A doctor's letter!" she said. "Of course he will listen."

*

At first Gill did not want to go as she had been to China during the Cultural Revolution but things had changed and I persuaded her to come with me.

Our team went to Beijing by separate routes. The younger members had decided to trek along the Great Wall while Gill and I went first to Xi'an and walked along the Li River near Guilin.

We reached a village where we heard loud laughter coming from an inn. A large crowd, perhaps the whole village, was clearly enjoying what was on television and we saw that it was our own, very British, *Absolutely Fabulous* with Jennifer Saunders and Joanna Lumley dubbed in a Chinese language, probably Mandarin.

The Chinese told me that, despite the considerable differences in lifestyle, *AbFab* was very popular there. The topsy turvy situation where the adults behave badly while the children act responsibly hit a chord and was extremely funny.

I had wondered whether the tonal Chinese languages might be more easily transmitted and interpreted in electrical terms than European consonants. If so, I had suggested, the Chinese deaf might do better with cochlear implants than their European counterparts. That thought was what may have led to our invitation to China where we taught a course in Beijing.

During the Cultural Revolution 'barefoot doctors' with a brief medical training were dispatched with whatever antibiotics happened to be available, some of which were dangerous to the hearing. They used them indiscriminately in people with coughs and sore throats with catastrophic results.

I had seen films made during that bizarre period showing patients having surgery while awake, acupuncture needles alone providing the pain control, and Gill had actually watched such an operation where the patient was entirely free of pain so I was anxious to know more.

"It was not true," the Chinese professor said. "It was faked. They were injected full of local anaesthetic before you came in."

I could not understand who had been fooling whom. We had been duped, of course, but after failed attempts at anaesthesia by acupuncture we had dropped the whole business. I cannot imagine such deception converting anyone to Maoism but someone must have thought it might do so.

I wondered if Mao too had been duped and I was reminded of the Lysenko affair when Stalin had been taken in by a scientist who had branded genetics as rubbish and claimed that evolution could be forced to produce better plants and, by implication, better human beings. Lysenko, inspired by Stalin's own theories, grew wheat in the north where only rye survived. The proof, which had shaken the scientific world as many left-leaning scientists had believed it, were plants with ears of both wheat and rye on the same stem. Lysenko, showered with prizes, had hundreds of Russian biologists sacked and sent to prison camps. Many perished there, including the geneticist Vavilov who died of starvation. I did not know what to make of all this at the time as some people assured me they had seen the plants.

In the mid 1960's, long after Stalin's death, Lysenko was exposed as a criminal con-man and the double stems of wheat and rye proved to have been crudely stuck together with glue. I had not imagined that anyone might get away with such a makeshift fabrication.

In China I had the chance to talk to someone who had participated in a similar deception, even if only by keeping his mouth shut, and I was anxious to find out something about how that happens. We all wonder what we would have done in similar circumstances.

The professor told me he had been working in a pig farm at the time as the senior doctors had been sent to rural areas for corrective labour with poor peasants.

I asked what he had gained from that experience.

"Nothing at all," he said, "absolutely nothing whatsoever."

*

The girl Bibi was aged nine when she was brought to see me.

The daughter of General Zia ul-Haq, President of Pakistan, yet another of the dictators which I was to come across.

I was told that they wanted her cured of her disabilities. Was I prepared to operate? If not, goodbye. There seemed to be no interest in other supporting or educational management.

When she arrived the little girl was very friendly and immediately climbed onto my lap and gave me a kiss.

The doctor who had come with her said she was a very amiable and affectionate child, liked by everyone, but he felt obliged to give an explanation regarding the background. He said that General Zia had had a traditional military career rising up the ranks as a reliable, honest and pious officer with a devoted wife and grown-up children who was looking forward to retirement when his wife gave birth to Bibi who had special needs. Soon after, the then Prime Minister, Zulfikar Ali Bhutto, appointed him Commander-in-Chief and Zia subsequently deposed him, saw him hanged, and became President. According to that doctor Zia associated Bibi's birth with providential favour and for practical purposes she had become like a mascot who could do as she pleased.

She was allowed to roam the palace freely and experienced great pleasure from running past the guards to trigger elaborate and noisy salutes and presenting of arms. She also enjoyed attending state receptions and dinners, running among the guests at tables, climbing on their laps, taking a mouthful off their plates and thanking them with a kiss. Fortunately she had an attractive and affable personality so nobody minded and neither did I. I was curious, however, and asked if she had got onto Mrs Thatcher's lap.

"Yes," said the doctor, "and she kissed Ronald Reagan."

"President Mitterand?"

"Oh yes, all of them," the doctor said, adding, "also Deng Xiaoping!"

It seems so improbable that I have been kissed so affectionately by a girl who had kissed Mrs Thatcher, Mr Mitterrand, Ronald Reagan, and all the world leaders including even Deng Xiaoping. But there you go.

*

In my youth, and I suppose my innocence, Marxism was best discussed late at night. Incomes would be according to need, education open to all, health care free from cradle to grave, there would be no competition for money or status and also it was inevitable. To be decided was the speed of the process, expedited, slowed down or ruthlessly imposed for the Greater Good. The discussions were tedious but the aim worthy and those I knew moved on to become professors of medicine, lawyers, and academics receiving an unexpected share of knighthoods and peerages, which is how the establishment absorbs apparently indigestible individuals.

I met an actual Russian, a real Soviet citizen, when I worked at the Whittington Hospital. A lowly employee of the Soviet Trade Delegation in Highgate, he was sitting in our secretary's office, his daughter was on our long tonsil waiting list and he had brought the secretary, Miss Branchetti, a perfume called *Moscow Nights*, which he said was all the rage in Russia.

I saw him in the office from time to time bringing a small gift for Miss Branchetti, and he told me that with waiting lists it is best to endear yourself to the person who actually posts the letters as cancellations provided an opportunity for his daughter's tonsillectomy, and it was the secretary who filled the vacancies.

"I pop in on my way home," he said, "and I befriend her, she has my telephone number."

That, he said, is what the Soviet system had taught him and winked at me.

That was not the last time that I had to do with the Soviet Trade Delegation as Mr Ivanov brought Mr Patolichev, the Soviet Minister of Foreign Trade, to see me in my private office in Harley Street many years later. His medical file, the results of extensive investigations and treatments, translated into English travelled with him and doctors all over the world had added their reports. It was a perk that his position in the Soviet government gave him.

"This is a very high standard of medicine," I said, hoping to help out my colleagues in Moscow. "Are all hospitals in the Soviet Union that good?"

"No!" the Minister said, taking my compliment as an insult and banged on my desk.

"No!" repeated Mr Ivanov. "Only special hospitals for Ministers and top Party dignitaries."

He wanted to make it clear he was not treated as an ordinary person in his country.

"Is like private, like Harley Street," Mr Ivanov said, "the Minister wants you to know."

When the Soviets had evaporated I operated on a Russian who owned a huge industrial concern, and when I came to see him before surgery he was walking about as if in a cage, his hospital gown open at the back, dictating or giving instructions to a little crowd with pencils and notebooks.

He invited me to visit Russia and stay with my wife while an aide produced pictures of his house. I said politely that it looked like a palace.

"It is a palace," the aide confirmed. "He is the prince now."

We did visit Leningrad just before it reverted to St Petersburg and the Kirov was already the Mariinsky Theatre again. We stayed at the old Leningrad Hotel and our windows opened on the battleship *Aurora* that had fired the first shots of the Bolshevik revolution and was now moored on the frozen Neva.

I had nothing more to do with Russia.

*

A call came from the Department of Defence on a Sunday evening.

"Er…", the voice said, "you are seeing a Libyan officer in Harley Street, er…tomorrow morning, er…"

"I am sorry," I said. "I haven't got my list with me."

The Minister, I was informed, would be very grateful if I did my best for him.

I always do my best for all my patients so I was naturally irritated, especially when it was intimated that the officer was here on a shopping expedition.

"You are selling them arms, is that it?" I asked.

"No, no!" he replied quickly. "They are vehicles."

"You mean tanks?"

"Not tanks, no," he said, "just specialised vehicles!"

He came the following morning with his GP who was extremely old and shuffled along painfully. I found out later that he was in his mid-80s.

"Abdul," he said to his patient whose name was not Abdul, "wait outside, I want to talk to the doctor privately."

The officer went out and stood in the corridor behind the door until we called him back.

"This is the stupidest man I have ever met," he said, pausing to get his breath back, "and he is the commander-in-chief of the Libyan Army so you must keep him alive at all costs."

Powerful people, particularly when insecure or paranoid, often surround themselves with stupid men. I suppose that those who are ambitious learn to hide their skills until they are ready to strike.

The commander-in-chief was very grateful and gave me a brass tray on which I still place my morning coffee.

"Please come to Libya," he had said when he left. "I want to introduce you to my President."

I did receive an invitation in due course when Gaddafi had a problem and my secretary received a call to check whether I was Jewish. She replied that the religion of Guy's consultants was not noted.

Everything to do with Colonel Gaddafi's Libya was murky and no one seemed to know what went on. That poor desert country suddenly acquired one of the highest incomes per head of its tiny population and it was healthcare that its people wanted most. As little was available locally, a huge influx of patients, many with diseases so uncommon or advanced that they are rarely seen here, arrived brandishing letters from the Libyan Embassy offering financial guarantees.

Real money was to be used only to pay our fees and the hospital invoices, as the total was deducted from the vast sums that the United Kingdom owed Libya for its oil as far as I understood. I had heard that Mrs Castle, our Secretary of State, had offered to treat Libyans on the NHS for a global fee though, with waiting lists and other problems, our system was not flexible enough.

The Embassy, however, simply did not pay. This was the first time such a thing had happened so the doctors, who had little financial understanding, were confused but continued to see patients as that is what they do when faced with very sick people, and hoped that with their huge oil wealth, the Libyans would pay up one day.

Private hospitals, some in the hands of American corporations, complained and threatened but their accusations were denied by the Libyan government who insisted that everyone had been paid.

The dispute became a crisis when a surgeon who had rooms in the same Harley Street building as I did tried to admit the wife of one of Gaddafi's aides as an emergency and the hospital demanded payment in advance.

Her husband, forced to look into it, discovered that the staff of the Libyan Embassy had sent the invoices to Tripoli for years and had received the money but, I was told, instead of paying the bills they had invested it on their own account. The longer the delay the more interest they collected, giving them a huge rolling fund.

After that events got quite bizarre as Gaddafi, I understood, fearing his embassy staff might run away and hide the money they had in secret bank accounts, set in place an elaborate plan.

Libyan agents calling themselves students suddenly occupied their own Embassy. One of them was a patient of mine and had always been suspected of spying on them by the real students. Gaddafi supported the so-called "students" and changed the name of the embassy to Libyan People's Bureau, which led to a standoff until a tragedy occurred when someone shot a young policewoman, Yvonne Fletcher, from the window of the embassy.

I heard that the staff, who had hoped for arrest by the British, had been taken back to Libya and tortured into revealing where they had hidden the money before we were finally paid but, as in all such situations, there are so many lies that I never knew what to believe.

*

There was, finally, a king who became part of those legends that hang around hospital wards and operating theatres at the end of a session when everyone is exhausted and having their tea. No one remembers who it was about or when it happened, if ever.

Walliker, the physicist in my team at Guy's, was exceptional and though his first name was John I always think of him as Walliker as John makes him sound ordinary. His most interesting quality was that as soon as he had achieved something he would want to improve it and could not resist upgrading, tweaking endlessly. I like to recall the search which has no end and which I can still pursue, on and on, even if only in my mind.

Walliker needed gold-plated electrodes and, true to his temperament, decided that he would make them himself, setting it up in his lab. He then presented me with a scalpel he had gold plated as a trial or perhaps just for fun. The instrument gleamed magically and I took it with me as I was on my way to perform an operation.

The patient had been booked into the Wellington, a private hospital in Northwest London where I operated occasionally. As I was not there often enough, the nursing director of the operating theatres did not consider me important when allocating sessions and I had to make do with those moments which happened to be free.

"The morning is quite impossible" was a constant refrain as Mr so-and-so was operating on a Sheikh or Mr this-and-that had a film star on the table, and she made it clear that I was at the end of the queue.

I gave my golden scalpel to a nurse to sterilise and the next time I came I handed her a small nasal speculum which Walliker had also gold-plated.

The director got curious.

"Yes," I said. "All my instruments have been made in solid gold and I will tell you about it if you give me a cup of tea and a biscuit."

I told her that I had operated on a King and that he had secretly obtained a list of all the instruments I used from my staff at Guy's Hospital and had them all cast in gold. He had given them to me, in gratitude, as a gift, the whole lot, scalpels, lots of artery forceps and even the larger retractors.

"They weigh a lot, of course, and I have to keep them in a bank vault otherwise the insurance would be inconceivable," I added, "but I like to take a small instrument now and again as it would be a pity to have them always hidden away. I will bring another one next time if you like."

I begged her not to spread it around as I might be liable for tax even though they were both tools of my trade and an unsolicited gift, but I never had problems with her again and there was always a cup of tea waiting when I arrived.

For many years I continued to hear some version of this story circulating round the operating theatres of London. If I expressed scepticism I have been assured that people had actually seen these solid gold surgical instruments. It may be that the tale will go on forever as such stories are a sort of Eldorado, and it is good that strange and golden things happen from time to time even if it is in our imagination.

The Wide World

'Beyond the Wild Wood comes the Wide World,' said the Rat. 'And that's something that doesn't matter, either to you or me. I've never been there, and I'm never going, nor you either, if you've got any sense at all.'
— Kenneth Grahame, *The Wind in the Willows*

I did find my way into the Wide World or was it rather that I had come from there? I suspect that it is both, but all cultures do well to meet at least to find out about one another. If we discover that there is also something that we can learn, all the better. Where science and medicine are concerned it is essential rather than a choice and, though I can't speak for those who might have learnt something from me, I certainly benefited from what I experienced elsewhere.

*

"You have to select a chairman and denote the language of your deliberations," the functionary of the European Commission told us in an accent hard to define but which made his words sound oddly weighty.

"He must be Flemish," someone whispered. "They have that weird tone."

We were in Brussels to determine what levels of noise would be permitted in the workplace and I was a British representative. In the 1980's, Europe was still small and manageable, and our decisions were to go to an economic committee to see if they were practical and then to a legal one for appropriate phrasing, and finally the Council had to pass it into law unanimously.

Although cumbersome it was straightforward as we all knew each other but it was clear that the chairman could not be from one of the bigger countries so I proposed the Dane. Later my brother, a civil servant who attended many such meetings, told me that the Danes were often a sort of surrogate British.

We had to agree on a single language, otherwise simultaneous translation would involve costly interpreters, and most delegates assumed it would be English. The French insisted on their own language.

I said I was happy with French. As everyone else sighed in dismay the French delegates replied that in that case they would accept English, which they spoke perfectly well.

They told me later that they had been instructed to agree to English only if French had been given due consideration. I had not been given any instructions whatsoever about anything.

Spain and Greece soon joined us and the Greek delegate asked to speak to me privately. Worried because the Socialists had come to power in Athens, he thought that since we had a Labour government, I might give him some tips. I pointed out that social democracy today was mainly rhetoric and that even Papandreou, their Prime Minister, might get earache.

He was beaming at our next meeting.

"He did! He did!" he said, slapping me on the back. "Like you said! Papandreou! He got earache!"

The Dutch delegate told us that all factories in Holland paid into a kitty which was used to compensate workers who had lost any hearing. This interested me as in the United Kingdom workers had to sue as individuals or as Class Actions, a cumbersome and costly process. The German said that "no-fault compensation" was unfair to the good companies who had to provide a share of the kitty even though they did not cause damage. The Dutch explained that inspectors checked the noise levels. The Greek said that inspectors could be bribed. The Dutchman was shocked at such a thought. That is how it went on.

I had decided to test some of the effects of excessively loud sound myself and took a group of medical students to the Round House in Camden Town where a band known for its loud music, I think it was *The Who*, was playing. We had equipment to record our own hearing before and after the show and we found a measurable drop in everyone's higher frequencies. Although this recovered within a few days I wondered if those who go regularly suffer lasting damage.

I do not know why so many fail to take the risk seriously and I once warned a Member of Parliament that he should stop shooting pheasants or he would become seriously deaf. He said that the important decisions in his Party at that time were made during shooting parties at the estate of a great Earl and he wanted to be there. He also rejected my suggestion that he wear ear defenders.

"That would be sissy!" he said.

I watched him get worse over the years though he did become a member of the cabinet and helped rule the country.

Young people have important social reasons for attending noisy concerts and that may be where they will meet future spouses and where the rest of their lives begin.

One restaurant was so noisy that we were unable to hear each other speak. It was due to the hard reflective surfaces, especially the mirrors, around us so I wrote to the owners offering my expertise on ways to reduce the background noise.

The reply was friendly, saying that they had taken advice on how to make the restaurant noisier as people liked the buzz that was created when everyone shouted. The owner did not eat there himself and suggested a few quiet places he liked.

When I was getting near retirement from clinical work I took on medico-legal work, much of which involved noise-induced deafness in the workplace.

"Are you familiar with the safety regulations?" one of the younger lawyers asked on the telephone.

"There is a booklet," he went on when I had said yes. "I can send you a copy."

"Thank you," I replied. "I have one."

He kept insisting. It was most important, he said, that I understood the principles and spirit behind the regulations.

"It is based on European legislation," he said, "which is spelt out in the booklet. Call me if you don't understand anything."

"I wrote the booklet," I said.

He was silent for a moment, then pointed out that a committee had written it.

"A committee is people," I said. "Someone writes it down."

I don't think he believed me.

*

My father feared instability in the Balkans, a region that had been at the origin of many wars, an abscess draining the debris of the old Ottoman Empire. Born in that ill-defined entity during its terminal crumbling years, its anxieties had lingered in his mind despite decades of calm, regardless of my insistence that nothing would happen there again. The area was so peaceful that no one now talked of the Balkans and many were not sure where they were.

Tranquility ended with the breakup of Yugoslavia and the International Crisis Group (ICG) asked me to go to Kosovo. I knew little about that organisation but I was impressed by the documentation they sent me and, having just retired from the NHS, I was happy to be of use. Our party consisted of an American associated with the Democratic Party, a former Finnish cabinet minister and me. My companions were members of the ICG and, if the reason for my presence was not spelled out, I assumed it was because I was a doctor, though it was also suggested that I actually knew what the Ottoman Empire had been.

We flew to Pristina, the capital of Kosovo and, met by the field worker, we were briefed on that small territory and on Macedonia, which we were also to visit. I was impressed by the quality of his work and analysis.

The ICG, I discovered, was funded by various governments and to a lesser extent by institutions, corporations and private individuals, and seemed to be as independent as any NGO (Non-Governmental Organisation) in what I saw of the collection and analysis of information. The prevention and resolution of conflict was their aim and they had influential people like Ambassadors Abramowitz and Pickering, Senator Mitchell and Lords Malloch Brown and Chris Patten. Their Balkan reports must have been useful to decision makers.

My life had been about treating sick individuals rather than administering health care, though I have also been an observer passing on what came my way, but I cannot tell if anyone ever paid any attention to my reflections. Diffident of giving advice, I longed for an operating theatre where I could do what I am good at, but there I was.

Pristina was a mess and at the hotel we carried our things up five flights as there was no electricity. I was particularly affected, because the buildings and homes were so similar to ours and the people wore the same clothes and looked like us. When places look different they may be distressing but it is the commonplace that startles. The question that inevitably came to mind was whether this could happen nearer home. Could the neighbours down the road violently turn against us in such a way, citing reasons esoteric and obscure to the outsider? Or none at all as reasons could not be substituted for deep, irrational hate? And yet, I had to accept that this was also happening not far off, in Northern Ireland.

I was appalled when I inspected the hospital. The director appointed by the World Health Organisation (WHO) was English and I was curious about him as I had wondered whether there was a place for me in that type of work.

An Accident and Emergency professor in the Midlands, he had been a volunteer in an earthquake relief operation for the WHO that led to his being asked again and he found he was good at it and enjoyed the thrill involved. I did not ask what his hospital back home thought about his frequent absences or if the NHS was obliged to accept them as part of our nation's contribution to the good of the world.

He told me that when he took over the hospital in Pristina he found Albanian and Serbian doctors shooting at each other in the corridors, and I did not understand how he got things under control. Whether he had called in the military or had locked himself in his office until they went away, or both, it was now so quiet that I wondered what was going on. Albanian doctors, I was told, had been refused jobs in the public hospitals and were accustomed to seeing patients in their homes or in private clinics, and the Serbian doctors had gone.

I monitored a young German lawyer taking evidence from people who had made war crime accusations to the Court in the Hague. A charming girl my children's age, keen to gain experience as she hoped to become a Human Rights lawyer, she wore blue jeans like most NGO's, but she had a crisp white shirt with a stiff collar giving her a formal air, proper for what she had to do. She prompted respect.

The process was demanding as everyone spoke through interpreters. Stories of repeated rape, multiple murder and of snipers shooting at children distressed us all and the witnesses were obviously anguished repeating what they had experienced.

I was unnerved, although I had read many documents in preparation, and I still go over it again and again in my mind trying to understand how ordinary people could behave as they did. The fact that their communities seemed identical to ours, cosmopolitan, cultured and diverse was chilling. It might happen anywhere, unless we recognise the danger signs and, remembering a story of the Spanish Civil War where people waited to ambush and kill those who lived across the street, I did not feel confident that I would be able to do so.

I had never come to terms with the method of calculated and systematic dehumanisation in the Holocaust and later I was shocked by the massacre in Rwanda, but what happened then in the former Yugoslavia and became known as ethnic cleansing seemed to present a similar type of outrage.

What was most difficult for me to make sense of was also what victims and witnesses repeated again and again. Those who raped them and killed their children were not anonymous thugs who had come from somewhere else and then disappeared into nowhere. It was neighbours, the postman with whom they always exchanged a few words about the weather, the bus driver who picked them up from work. I was unexpectedly upset when I heard that employees were shot at by familiar snipers on their way to work at the *Holliday Inn*. The *Holliday Inn*, for God's sake!

Witnesses kept interrupting their own evidence to ask us why that had been done to them, as if we might have discovered something or identified a reason that had eluded them, but I got the impression that such questions dominated their thoughts. It was also a question that, as far as I know, none of the perpetrators, mostly Serbs, answered other than in apocalyptic terms referring to a monstrously distorted Greater Historical Justice which they, ordinary men, should not be asked to explain. They were sure only that they had done their duty, what seemed the right thing to do at the time. I wondered if they would ever change their minds or always feel justified about their past actions.

The young lawyers from the United States, Italy, Germany and elsewhere were impressive and there was not much that I could contribute but I noticed that occasionally everyone concerned, victims, witnesses and interpreters as well as the lawyers who took the depositions were so overcome that details, such as exactly which day reported events had taken place, were left uncertain. I knew what could be made with alibis by the defence if the wrong date was given and I urged them to be precise.

I was overcome by a feeling that we should protect these young investigators from knowledge of such horrible things much as we try to shield our children from information that they are not yet able to handle. But it is their world now and not my generation's. It is they who will have to deal with it, not me.

"It is very important," the German girl said, "that we get to the bottom of what happened. Especially for us Germans."

"What do you mean?" I asked.

"Few of us," she replied, "know exactly what our grandparents did in the second World War, much less what they were thinking. Even if they were not aware it is not clear how they felt and some even say they can't remember, but we have to live with them."

We went on to Macedonia as huge numbers of Albanian refugees from the wars in Kosovo, more than 300,000 people, were living in camps. In fact, as soon as NATO intervened the refugees went home and those concerns evaporated, leaving us to question what had been going on there in the first place.

The majority of the population were 'Macedonians', a Slavic people who are close in history and language to Bulgarians while an Albanian minority claimed they were being repressed. Their number was not clear as they said they were 40% of the population while the Macedonians insisted the figure was only 20%. The capital Skopje's most famous citizen was Mother Theresa, an Albanian, and we stayed at the main hotel, the *Alexander the Great*, a name that infuriated the Greeks who insisted that these people should not even be allowed to call themselves Macedonians at all since, as far as the Greeks were concerned, they were nothing but second-rate Bulgarians, if that.

Without even counting the Gypsies, this complex situation would have been laughable if we had not been aware that it could explode into civil war and some of the decent and welcoming people who were our hosts might start raping and murdering their neighbours.

To a large extent it was the stuff of the proliferating analysts and NGO's, bright young people with degrees from top universities who document and interpret facts in such detail that we can take their reports home and by the following morning know everything about a region, its history, demography, economics and political parties even though we may never even have heard of it before. Some are so good at uncovering facts that they are feared by governments who may arrest or deport them.

Despite a lifetime taking care of people at their most vulnerable, I must have failed to grasp what lies at the deepest level. I absorbed facts well enough to lecture on the Balkans from Ottoman times to the Kosovo war and describe what I saw, but I have not understood why and how ordinary people could engage in such crimes against other ordinary people, many of whom they know, in places, even, where we went on holiday. After all, the Winter Olympics were held in Sarajevo not that long ago.

It is not for want of theories but, as every time I reflect on them they seem inadequate, I keep them to myself.

*

I rarely consult the Bible before traveling but I had been asked to teach a course in Basra, in southern Iraq not far from the headwaters of the Shatt el-Arab, a wide waterway that leads to the Persian Gulf. Its claim to be the site of the Garden of Eden helped me accept the invitation, a chance to go where our culture might well have started and to see the ruins of Sumer, Abraham's legendary home. Basra was a quiet, even sleepy city then, just before Iraq invaded Iran initiating eight years of war and destruction.

We flew over desert and then over patches of lush greenery around streams and rivulets, and I looked for the five rivers mentioned in the Bible. The Euphrates and the Tigris are easy to identify from the air but not *the Pishon which flowed round the whole land of Havilah, where there is gold* or the *Gihon that flows round the whole land of Cush.* What, for that matter, are Havilah and Cush called today? Do they exist or have they been taken over by the waters or the deserts?

I was taken to a beautiful green picnic spot where a nabuc tree grew. They called it Adam's tree as it was said to have borne the Forbidden Fruit, which now was small, pale yellow and bitter and available by the basketful for sightseers. The few who were there seemed to enjoy the idea of things forbidden as well as the fun of simple curiosity. I understood that the story as told in the Koran does not specifically blame Eve for original sin but that she and Adam had joint responsibility for the turnaround of mankind.

It may be a poetic account of self-awareness, sin and shame and associated with the change from a hunter-gatherer lifestyle to that of agriculturalists. No doubt farming people required a better-regulated society in a moral sense as well as division of labour.

I worked very hard while I was in Iraq and they made greater use of me than I had bargained for so, wanting to make the most of my stay, I asked to visit Ur of the Chaldees as well as the people who were known as the marsh Arabs.

Ur, possibly the first city ever, did not need digging up as its citizens had simply gone away, its buildings and its ziggurat a sort of mini-tower of Babel, gradually falling to ruin. Oddly moved by the broken crockery, residue of the lives of people from whom I may even be descended that lay strewn all over the place, I tried to count the generations. Not that many, as with three taking up a century, their names might have hardly filled a page.

The remains of the vivid and colourful city are now only ruins, sand and broken potsherds, all in tones of yellowish beige, the overcast sky reflecting the same dull, oppressive shade.

Surrounded by antiquity, immoderate thoughts crept in on me. The origins of civilisation, the roots of Western society and even the meaning of culture, so I did not notice the figure jumping lithely from one building to another and when I finally did so I thought it was a monkey. As he came towards me I saw an old man with a limp.

"My father," he said, "he dig with English Willy! Me guide now."

It took a moment before I worked out that English Willy must have been Sir Leonard Woolley, who had identified these ruins as Ur of the Chaldees and had found evidence of a great flood. There was much excitement at the time as ancient tablets told an epic tale where Gilgamesh, a hero-king, also had to face the catastrophic flood that decimated mankind. This seemed to confirm the biblical story of Noah and a few even claimed it must have been one and the same man.

"This Abraham house," the old man said, indicating a pile of yellow bricks.

I must have looked doubtful as he began gesticulating and pointing.

"You know Moon God?" he asked. "He called Nana. You know him?"

"Not very well."

"Never mind." The old man looked uncertain but then rallied. "Abraham not like Nana. He say no good. You know Sun God, Shamash? Abraham not like also so he go away to Mecca!"

I did not argue about one myth or the other but it made me think of the impact of ancient floods, as Gilgamesh is inspired to seek immortality, and when he fails he turns to construction work instead as he believes it is buildings that last forever.

Noah's morality is more appropriate than a wish to live forever, though to his credit, Gilgamesh abandoned that particular project. Adam is given six rules to live by which are later included in the Ten Commandments and Noah, as part of the bargain to avoid another destruction of mankind, is given a seventh, the requirement to have just laws. I suppose it is that condition which has led directly to Human Rights legislation.

The local paediatrician took me to the marsh Arabs as it was him they trusted most. I was particularly anxious to meet clans that were reputed to worship the Devil as I wondered what such a concept might offer.

Alexander the Great brought with him philosophers as well as soldiers so they might investigate any new deity they came across, especially those with attributes they had not known before and whose understanding might prove helpful.

New gods are new ways of looking at life and though it is remarkable that they did this more than 20 centuries ago, it is not surprising as the

Greeks gave us tales such as that of Oedipus, which we still use to describe our own behaviour and emotions.

The marshes were one of the most extraordinary places I have ever seen. The inhabitants lived their lives around the long reeds that grow out of the shallow waters and their dwellings were made of the stems which were tied, bent or woven but despite a rickety appearance the interiors were very cozy, with carpets covering the floor. Some of the houses had been fashioned on floating islands made of reeds and mud and were very comfortable inside.

People wandered among them in boats punted by long poles, tending buffaloes, farming small rice paddies, fishing while a few worked at weaving the ubiquitous reeds.

They welcomed us when I bought some of their produce, and invited us in for tea or coffee. Finding Devil Worshippers who would talk to me was a problem, however, as they seemed reticent to promote themselves under that title and the paediatrician, acting as interpreter, said that their Sheikh denied they worshiped Shaytan, or Satan.

As that was the purpose of my visit I was not sure what to say until he elaborated.

"Of course we don't worship the Devil!" the Sheikh said. "Who does? It is just that we respect him as he shows up God who treats us capriciously."

I had never heard that particular criticism and my excitement at discovering a new insight must have been similar to that of the Hellenistic philosopher who had a new deity to report to Alexander, so I began by raising Satan's first crime, the temptation of Eve and Adam.

"That is a perfect example!" said the Sheikh. "Had Eve not eaten the forbidden fruit what would we have been now? Animals, pets with no awareness! She saved us from that."

His knowledge of biblical arguments was greater than mine and his views so original that he got the better of me. Satan's cruelty towards Job was turned around by pointing out there was no reason why God should have gone along with such persecution.

He was particularly bitter about God's collusion with Jacob in buying his seniority from his older brother Esau and tricking his blind old father Isaac.

"What is that sort of behaviour?" he said, shaking his head. "God treats the world whimsically and only Satan shows him up. That is why we respect him."

*

I was taken by surprise when I landed in Istanbul. Driven from the airport I had barely glanced at the street signs, meaningless to me, except for one pointing to 'Kadiköy'.

I was startled as I did not think that place really existed. The sound, with lots of hard consonants and ending with 'oy', had always been faraway stuff. Fairy tales and my grandmother's stories.

Kadiköy was where she had come from and where her father had been a teacher at the *Alliance Israelite* school in the 19th century. He had taught French to Jewish children in an attempt to free them from the sleepy Ottoman world and point them towards Western enlightenment. That is why French ended up as my first language.

Invited to teach a course at the Gulhane Military Medical Academy, my emotions had been stirred by my arrival, three generations later, as if to display the ultimate result of his work. Named Eugénie after the French Empress, my grandmother had read to us from the *Contes* by Perrault but I could never unpick them from the equally imaginative stories from her own schooldays. Places such as Ortaköy on the European side of the Bosphorus or Üsküdar and Kadiköy on the mysterious Anatolian coast had seemed as unreal as the *Contes*, and I could not tell between her family holidays on Prinkipo in the Sea of Marmara and the castle of *Barbe Bleue*.

When the driver pointed out the Pera fire tower I recalled her calling out "Istanbul is on fire!" in Turkish, her pitch raised and the volume lowered as if from afar, when she told us of nights in tents in the earthquake of 1912.

As I was no Turk my hosts were puzzled when I tried to explain, so I got on with my work and they made the most of my visit, starting rounds at 6.30 in the morning.

Operations were televised and transmitted live to Ankara, Konia and other cities where viewers were encouraged to ask questions through an interpreter. It was the first time I had seen this done and I enjoyed explaining as I worked, but the questions were too numerous so we left them to the end.

I was exhausted after giving lectures each afternoon and so were the Turks, though feeling obliged to entertain me they asked if I wanted to go to nightclubs or dine watching belly dancers. They were relieved when I said that my cousin happened to be the French ambassador and that it would be very rude if I did not dine with him.

We should both have been named after our grandfather Eliahu, a biblical name that was then too old-fashioned, so I became Ellis instead and my cousin eventually turned into Eric. We both kept the 'E' at any rate. I dined every night with him and his aristocratic French wife at the Embassy including, amid great festivities, the 200th anniversary of the French Revolution.

That was a very stylish evening and I watched *Jeux de l'Amour et du Hazard*, an 18th-century drama by Marivaux, put on in a marquee in the vast garden by a theatre company shipped over from Paris though it was poorly attended, the guests wandering about the gardens attracted by more popular artists and bands, helping themselves from lavish tables.

I was talking to the actors when we were joined by a military delegation that happened to be in Turkey, and I discussed the meaning and nature of drama with a French general who had assumed I was a member of the theatrical company, but he was so attentive to my views that I felt it was unfair to deceive him and I confessed I was only a British surgeon.

He looked offended for a moment so I said that he had made me realise that I was an actor of sorts since I worked in an operating *theatre*, and he took it in good part.

"We too," he said, "perform in a *theatre* of war. There must be something behind all this though it escapes me for the moment. We should both reflect on our role in life. Was it not your Bard who pointed out that all the world's a stage? Everyone is an actor!"

Eric called me to the reception hall, as he was about to decorate an extremely aged Turkish poet with the *Légion d'Honeur*. The recipient was a close friend of France so members of the Turkish government were present as Eric began his formal speech '*Au nom de la République…*' and kissed the wavering old man on both cheeks as he was helped up from his wheelchair.

In a tremulous voice the poet responded "*La France…ma deuxième patrie…*" but he was soon moved to tears by the thought of France, or by the volatility of age, and everyone patted him gently to calm him down as he was lowered, sobbing, back into his chair.

The emotion of the moment passed when one of the Turkish ministers, I cannot remember if it was Health or Defence, presented me too with a medal and I was taken unawares when he embraced and kissed me. The large bronze medal was in a red velvet box and bore the image of Kemal Ataturk. Apart from those won for swimming when I was 12, it was the only medal presented to me and they all got lost in one move or another and, though I did not care then, I regret it now. Perhaps, as with the Turkish poet, age adds value to such expressions and even though I cannot think what I would have done with my swimming medals I am sorry I lost them all. Maybe they are still around in a shop that sells bric-a-brac or they already lie in a landfill which will be excavated in a thousand years. I hope my medal with the effigy of Ataturk will turn up one day.

Fireworks by Jean-Michel Jarre coloured the sky red, white and blue at the end of the evening and as the band struck '*Allons enfants de la patrie…*' my cousin's tall silhouette, his slim fashionable wife by his side, stood out against the changing colours and strange notions took hold of me. I commented out loud that we could never have imagined what was to come when we played as children on the banks of the Nile and perhaps, if the chips had fallen otherwise, I might even have been the French ambassador myself.

"And I might have been a London surgeon!" my cousin replied.

*

My last memory of Istanbul was on a later occasion and is a beautiful one as I watched the sunset, sipping *arak* with a group of foreign surgeons. The Golden Horn's name must have come from such moments as the reflection of the evening sun on the water glows as though it were gold.

Whether fatigue after excitement or the relief when good work is done or perhaps it was only the effect of the *arak*, but our mood turned reflective. Maybe it was that we were going home, doctors who had felt as one for a few days, disbanding and melting away into the reality of life, performing operations rather than talking about them. We held on to one another a while longer by sharing anxieties just as we had been sharing scientific ideas.

"Reagan," the Americans said after conferring among themselves, "is past it. He can hardly remember a thing. Scowcroft and those guys write everything he has to say on cards he looks at one at a time."

We were silent for a moment, if not entirely surprised, as doctors often pass such information on to each other.

"Chernenko is blue!" This time it was one of the Russian doctors who had spoken, his friends nodding confirmation, as the rest of us waited, expecting more.

"He cannot breathe!" The Russians were animated now. "He cannot walk. They hold him up for the Kremlin balcony!"

We were thoughtful, unsure what all this meant until an Italian doctor, a professor from Milan, spoke.

"The emperor of the west and the emperor of the east," he said, shrugging his shoulders. "Poor world."

*

There is some doubt about the Gulf. Is it Persian or Arab? It matters to them and it mattered to me as I flew towards Abu Dhabi.

We landed at night and I took my place in the queue but I was picked out by a portly man in white robes and nodded through.

"You doctor for Sheikh," he said, a statement rather than a question.

"How did you know it was me?" I asked.

"You not look like oil man," he replied, studying me carefully.

He took me to a black Mercedes and we drove through the city, inviting with its cheerful lighting, into the pitch black of the desert.

We drove in total darkness for an hour and I was getting restless because there were no other cars on the desert road. What happened if we broke down?

"Is it far?" I asked, but he only shrugged.

He must have been aware of my increasing anxiety as he spoke again.

"We are going to al-Ain. Is nice."

I remembered enough Arabic to recognise the meaning of the word.

"An oasis?" I asked.

"Yes," he replied after pondering for a while. "You know Buraimi oasis?"

"The empty quarter of Arabia?" Again, he must have sensed I was nervous as we drove deeper into the night and he tried to sound reassuring.

"Is like going to the country!" he said, pleased with his knowledge of English life.

Eventually I saw a faint orange glow in the distance, alarming by contrast with the blackness. It took more form as we got closer, suggesting human activity in the emptiness.

"Is that it? Are we there?" I asked.

"Al-Ain!" he replied, and now the orange light defined clear, recognisable words.

"HILTON HOTEL."

I had never imagined that the Hilton would one day represent civilisation or that the name should be so welcome, but I slept in comfort and in the morning I was up and dressed. The Lebanese concierge suggested I take my time and have a leisurely breakfast by the pool.

"Or even better," he said, "why don't you have a swim; you can get a costume from the hotel shop. Unwind, we will call you."

I swam up and down watched by white robed men flicking prayer beads and sipping coffee. After I had dried myself in the sun one of them came up to ask when I planned to visit the Sheikh, though he seemed very relaxed and gave the impression that no appointment book was kept and that I was expected to come along whenever I felt up to it.

The reverse is also true as the welcoming expression 'my house is your house' has an unexpressed consequence as accepting hospitality means 'your house is also my house and you may expect me at any time', a culture that is tiresome to us.

If the Sheikh did not mind being kept waiting he did not expect me to mind waiting in my turn. I was shown through a little door in the drab wall of the palace into a room heavy with English furniture, a floral Wilton carpet and Sanderson wallpaper where I was plied with coffee by a servant who poured again as soon as I emptied my cup.

I understood that the Sheikh's son would come to fetch me though they did not say when as there was little sense of time, of booked appointments or, as it turned out, of set meals but eventually a handsome young man in white robes and sparkling turban came in.

"DO- YOU- SPEAK- ENGLISH?" I said slowly, adding gestures to make myself clear.

"Actually," he said, pausing for a moment, "I have just come down from Oxford. I believe I may have come across your son, Danny, there."

It was difficult to understand what was going on as people came in and out, doing various jobs, and it was not clear which were members of the family and which were the servants. There was no attempt to introduce me to anyone or to explain the social setup. I felt that, although very courteous, they wanted to have as little to do with me as they could, expecting me to do my job and go.

Our medical training makes probing into the patient's social and psychological history essential and not to do so is remiss. Being reduced to a technician made me think about my role in a way I had not done before.

I wondered what they thought of me. Did they try to imagine my life as I did theirs? Were they curious? I suspected that they were not and that I was an unavoidable intruder, whose skills were needed but who should be thanked and paid off as soon as possible.

They habitually did not tell all about their medical condition or injury, revealing only as much as they thought was necessary and often withheld information that mattered, though I rarely understood their reasons for secretiveness.

I was presented with a huge gold watch with a gold strap encrusted with numerous small turquoises and other stones when I had finished. I had rarely seen anything I found less appealing, but it was discourteous not to accept any gift at all so I suggested instead a perfume for my wife.

"Yes," they agreed in one voice, satisfied by my request. "We say here: *make a man's wife content and she will make him happy*!"

On my return to Heathrow I was stopped by officers who wanted to know if I had received any cash, and I said that the revenue would be informed when my fee was paid.

"Did they give you a watch?" they insisted. "You have to declare such items."

"It was not to my taste so I did not take it," I said, and they let me pass.

Another doctor who had accepted the watch was asked for £2,000 duty. Flustered and unwilling to abandon it, he gave his credit card but his wife was furious and took it to the jewellers in one of the hotels in Park Lane hoping to recoup the money. They offered her £2,000.

"That Sheikh gave it to you, didn't he?" they said to her. "We know what duty you had to pay."

*

I was asked to visit another Gulf state where the ruler had lost his voice. I said there were better people to deal with cancer but they insisted.

"We know he hasn't got cancer," the director of their London office had said. "Many specialists from Europe and America have been already but his voice has still not come back so we need you to sort him out."

I felt slighted they had called me only when there was nothing serious but Jackie Barnes, my secretary, insisted I go. At my age, she said, I should feel honoured, not snubbed.

She also said something about taxi drivers not being allowed to refuse fares and lawyers having to defend criminals whether they liked it or not.

The ruler, a kindly elderly man, was obviously under stress but denied that anything was troubling him. The interpreter said that he had been told to show me whatever I wanted to see and to tell me whatever I wanted to know, so I questioned him instead.

The ruler had chaired a gathering of heads of state where the leaders had shouted accusations and insults at each other and he had had to raise his voice, though even then he had not been able to control the meeting. Apart from the strain on his vocal cords he had been offended by the discourtesy of the participants and felt responsible for the failure of the discussions.

I told the ruler not to speak, not even in a whisper, for a whole week and then start very, very quietly. I thought that resting his vocal cords and keeping away from what appeared to be a difficult job might break a vicious circle. He insisted on a prescription so I got the pharmacist to prepare a harmless saline spray.

I was there three days, promising to return if necessary. The interpreter, keen to make the most of my visit, wanted to eat in the best places and to take me to the malls but when I said I was not interested in shopping, he suggested 'antiquities' of which there was only one, a large ruin in the desert that was believed to have been a palace.

That was not likely, as only Bedouin had lived there until oil was discovered and, wandering among the rubble, I realised that it had been a caravanserai. I had seen similar ruins along the old roads from Turkey to Morocco in varying stages of dilapidation, though still evocative and even moving. It may have had something to do with the passage of time and the way things change as that always affects me.

When goods were carried on camels, they travelled in caravans protected by armed outriders we would now call security guards, and sheltered at night in the caravanserai along the way. These were defensive enclosures with strong gates that would be closed at nightfall and opened again at dawn when the caravan was ready to set off. An interior yard surrounded by arches where men and animals bedded down inspires serenity. Perhaps it is the regularity of a repetitive pattern that gives that effect to the architecture, especially when curves add softness.

As we drove back through the desert I tried to tell my escort that the Gulf's location on the trade routes from India and China had made it matter to the world. The changes that took place when the railways came and then the Suez Canal meant that there were no longer camels to house in the caravanserai, which were abandoned to the sand, and even their purpose forgotten. The interpreter had little idea of his own history, or pretended not to as it seemed to embarrass him, and he preferred to talk of modern development. He pointed to the miles of complex metal piping and cylindrical containers where the oil was stored, as well as the wells which stretched into the desert beyond the horizon, burning off gas.

It occurred to me that when the oil ran out everything would be abandoned like the caravanserai, rusting in the sand, their function forgotten, and perhaps a visitor would be told these had been palaces.

The exhausted old ruler got better. Three days later he said he was cured but was pleased when I still forbade him to speak till the end of the week. Powerful people feel comforted when they are given strict instructions by the doctor.

"Was it all in the head?" the interpreter asked discretely.

"God only knows," I replied, "but he will get better anyway."

"*Inshallah*!" he said. "May it be God's will."

"*Inshallah!*" I confirmed.

*

We had been invited to hire academic gowns from a shop in the town if we had not brought our own, as the participants to that conference were expected to dress up. It had seemed silly and I was taken aback when I discovered that all those of the Royal College of Surgeons had gone already. I took what was left and hoped no one would notice, whispering an embarrassed explanation to someone amused to find me gowned as a *docent* of some Scandinavian university.

"Don't worry my dear fellow," he said, pointing to his own resplendent blue silk and ermine robe with a funny little tasseled hat, "no one is wearing the right one. I picked the prettiest, Doctor of Theology from somewhere, I believe. Could be Leipzig!"

Everyone was delighted in our colourful group and our pictures were put in the local paper.

Respected surgeons set up forums where they would honour and grant each other awards. At the start of my career I was told to invite mainly those who had the authority to invite us back.

"Don't waste your time with the others," I was instructed. "You scratch their back so they'll scratch yours!"

I was unable to take this advice so I never got to be an organiser and I had to rely on my own contributions to get invited at all, but there may have been an element of laziness on my part. For years I pretended, even believed, that it was a matter of principle but I hardly saved democracy.

Changes took place over the years as initially arrangements were always made for wives. Gifts were offered, Hermes scarves on one occasion in Paris, and visits to museums or fashion shows arranged to occupy them when their husbands were engaged in medical meetings. When female surgeons increased in number and they brought their husbands, there was some uncertainty as these had to be classified as 'wives', but soon the term 'spouses' appeared and fashion shows were abandoned, though the men had quite liked to go. Even that changed as participants began to bring lovers, sometimes of the same sex, so the official idiom has become 'accompanying person' and it is now inappropriate to enquire whether people are married or not. We were a reflection of society in general.

The place of sponsors also changed, as initially drug companies were solicited for financial contributions but in time this was considered unacceptable as they might exert undue influence, so in some countries the government funded the meetings. I thought the French government the most bizarre as they were prepared to pay the enormous costs of simultaneous translation to make sure the French language remained official when English had long become the language of science.

Contact with different countries brought out the particularities of each one which taught us both how to act and what things are best avoided.

*

They have always said that in America the streets are paved with gold, and I believe it is true if you are prepared to work.

People who have never been there have strong views and often make unfavourable comments. As my children and grandchildren live there I face such declarations from time to time, occasionally from other Americans.

To those who insist that they could not possibly be part of that kind of world there is nothing I can say other than that, in that case, they had better not go, or mutter under my breath that as it is a whole continent, like the curate's egg, it may be good in parts.

After World War II America's success threatened the intellectual left and those who sought teaching posts there were suspected of betraying the liberal social outlook for the gold which, of course, paved the streets. American academics shared this view.

On the other hand the United States was so far ahead in science and medicine that a spell there was inevitable and the abbreviation BTA, for 'Been to America', was added, not entirely in jest, to the MRCP and FRCS of anyone with ambition.

I shared these mixed feelings though, in my case, America began with a series of misunderstandings as I ended up in the wrong city on my first visit.

I had obtained a credit card but, uncertain how it worked, I decided to limit my first meal at JFK Airport to a sandwich for just one dollar. Frugality, I had hoped, would see me through my visit so I got anxious when the waiter brought soup and coffee. He said it went with the sandwich but then came a huge oval dish piled high with salad, vegetables and meat. I was sure the waiter had misunderstood but he insisted it was my sandwich.

"Where is the bread, then?" I asked defiantly.

"Underneath!" he said impatiently, as in New York they do not suffer fools and he had reassured me once already.

The bill had really been only a dollar so I thought I might cope in America despite my dread of rampant capitalism.

"You working for Kodak?" the man on the connecting flight to Rochester asked.

"No," I replied.

"You must work for Kodak!" he insisted. "What else is there in Rochester?"

I thought he must be mad but another passenger explained that everyone on our flight worked for Kodak, so I said I was going to the Mayo Clinic.

"That is in Rochester, Minnesota," all the passengers called out. "We are going to Rochester, New York!"

It was not my first such mistake as I had once gone to the wrong country, inattentively boarding the boat train to Belgium instead of France. On that occasion I had irked the stationmaster by asking what I should do in Ostend until the next train to Paris.

"*Eh bien, monsieur*," he had replied with contempt, "you can go to the cinema for all I care!"

Though offended by his tone I saw a film with Sophia Loren.

This time I was in a strange continent with an unfamiliar credit card, but they helped me transfer and no one was rude or implied that flying to the wrong city had been anything other than a minor oversight.

Our hosts at the Mayo Clinic did everything they could to make us enjoy our stay, putting on a barbecue the highlight of which was a bonfire and a blue grass band.

It was decided that each group would sing a song from their own country and I was dragged forward with two neurologists, Roger Gilliat and Peter Thomas. Fortunately the latter could sing and led us in a wild rendering of *Men of Harlech*. Two female doctors from Hong Kong gave a bad version of *Love is a Many Splendored Thing* and I had begun to enjoy American ways.

I went on to Dallas where I visited the museum in the worst taste that I had ever seen showing a continuous film of the Kennedy assassination, then still fresh in our minds. A British cosmetic surgeon who invited me to supper had done well with breast enhancements. People mocked him as the "tit man" but their comments were tinged with jealousy and he took it in good part, pleased to show off his palatial home.

I could not explain the pleasant coolness of his Texas garden under a sky full of stars when everywhere else was unbearably hot, until I was told we were in an air-conditioned environment enclosed in a thin bubble made with the transparent implant material used for breasts. The company that made it was said to have given it to him in recognition. I was so amazed that I described it to colleagues later.

"Everyone knows about it," they said, "we call it the Big Tit!"

I asked a surgeon from Oklahoma to explain something about a new operation he was doing and he insisted on taking me home to show me before I flew on.

I ended up in California, a magic land. In Los Angeles I visited the House Clinic where I found the doctors warm, friendly and incredibly laidback. They had introduced new techniques and I was excited at what I would bring back to Guy's.

Victor Goodhill, another surgeon, had told me to meet him at Century Hospital. I had driven along avenues with romantic names that I knew from the cinema like Sunset Boulevard, Rodeo Drive and Wilshire, and found him waiting among the palm trees wearing a colourful Hawaiian shirt. It was all the stuff of films and I had a sudden impulse to stay forever. When I am particularly tired or it rains in Hampstead or perhaps simply when melancholy takes hold, I wonder if it might have been a better life.

Goodhill, white-bearded and famous for his surgical skills, had recently become a rabbi as well, so everyone spoke of him with the reverence afforded a prophet who transmitted the Word through ear surgery. In California that seemed not only possible but likely.

My trips to America became so frequent that I became known there and I came across outstanding surgeons from whom I continued to learn and who became lasting friends.

It is when coming across differences that we gain most, by contact with new ways of thinking that we can adapt for ourselves or that we can dismiss. At Guy's we had a close relationship with a number of American institutions, especially Johns Hopkins in Baltimore where I was to spend time as a visiting professor. We also arranged for each one of the ENT registrars to spend a year in Seattle in exchange for an American resident who came to us.

Although I saw the best medicine in the world, there was much wrong with access to health care in the US. This suggested that social progress might not have that much to do with the quality of medicine or with scientific progress and might even thwart them, an awful thought which went against all that I believed.

A major feature of American medicine, I discovered, is immigration. Britain encouraged immigration by doctors, especially from the Indian sub-continent, as far back as the 1950's but though they were said to come for training they were really here to provide a service. There was then no attempt to attract the best with permanent senior positions and status, which were to be reserved only for the British themselves. That was considered by everyone to be only proper and, as one said, "If you don't like it you needn't come."

Doctors from all over the world poured into America where they got the best, the most innovative and probably the pluckiest, as it takes courage to leave one's home for the unknown. The aim was to get the best they could.

Dr Abe Shulman of New York, who became a close friend, was to transform the study and understanding of tinnitus, a distressing ringing in the ears, on a truly international scale. I too became the subject of his forceful encouragement in the face of the negativity I sometimes found at home, as one of his enterprises was to bring together innovative people no matter where they came from or how unlikely their ideas might seem.

My longest stay in America was as visiting professor at Johns Hopkins in Baltimore, which is a wonderful place, and I was very happy there.

One of my duties was to have breakfast with the residents early in the morning so they could pick my brains. They wanted to know how we treated gunshot wounds of the head and neck and were shocked when I said that I was not the one to ask as in my whole career at Guy's or anywhere else, we had only had one case.

On that occasion I called my colleagues in Belfast and they told me what to do. Sadly it was a time of murderous violence in Northern Ireland.

At Hopkins they had at least one shooting in the head or neck every night as well as those of the chest, abdomen or limbs. I told them it was because we had relatively few guns on the street that our attackers had to make do with knives and broken bottles. "Gubbing", or aiming for the neck with the jagged edges, produced serious injuries and occasional fatalities on Friday nights and I had no doubt that if guns came their way they would use them.

Another of my duties was to give a series of lectures for postgraduates as well as graduates. I gave one a week and they were extremely well attended as many practitioners came from Baltimore and elsewhere in Maryland and Washington DC, so we had to move to a larger auditorium. This was very gratifying especially as my hosts at Hopkins were pleased with the large numbers I drew, though I suspect that many of these doctors may have received points for attending such lectures.

My last lecture had unexpected results.

I talked about the great surgeons who had taught me during my training, their personalities and their humanity. This was greeted with considerable interest as most of them were well known, at least by name, and my audience was pleased and sometimes diverted to learn more from someone who had met them. I was doing well until I said that I would tell them also about the bad surgeons I had come across, though not by name, as we can learn how not to do things too. This time I was faced with icy silence and although I still think I had a point to make, you just do not mention mistakes in America. Certainly not in public.

In New York I stood among a crowd of people in the reception area of a large public hospital when a woman pulled at my trouser leg. She had been sitting on the floor as there were not enough benches and spoke to me in French.

It was chance that she picked me as I doubt many in that hospital spoke that language. She was Haitian, escaping whatever circumstances she had come from, and had been told that she had cancer. The doctor had given her a booklet and told her to come back after she had read it, but she said that she did not read English.

The text, long and verbose, said more or less that she could have surgery or radiotherapy, surgery followed by radiotherapy, radiotherapy followed by surgery as well as chemotherapy. It also detailed the side effects. I asked her how old she thought the doctor might be. Young, she said.

I said to go back and ask him, "If I was your mother what would you do?"

It seemed wrong to have to do that, and yet.

And yet the treatment she would get may well be the best available in the world. America is like that.

I have always enjoyed going there. I have liked to wait at the corner of Landon Lane in Bethesda, Maryland and watch my grandchildren emerge from the yellow bus that brought them home from their elementary school, wondering what, if anything, my own story will mean to them.

And of course there is also Santa Monica where Gill and I walked along the beach on the mild and sunny February morning and stopped for coffee at Perry's.

*

A form of preferential treatment still plagues Italy as it sometimes excludes outstanding surgeons from the top positions in favour of those with an obscure political pull. The best ones often leave for Switzerland, America, Canada and countries where merit rules and where they have a better chance.

Ronald Raven, one of our consultants when I was a medical student, had returned from a visit to Italy and insisted on telling us how his Roman colleague was treated with respect by his students.

Mr Raven was a fine surgeon, though he enjoyed putting on an act of supreme arrogance. At least I was sure it was an act, as I could not believe his extreme statements could be anything but a spoof.

He had been envious of the way the students had clustered around the Roman professor when he arrived in the morning and helped him on with his white coat.

"We will help you sir!" they cried out. "We will help you on with your coat!"

We did wonder about him in the end when he decided to operate on his own father as he said he wanted the best surgeon for him, which he was sure was himself.

That episode came back to mind when a visiting Italian was sent up from Accident and Emergency to my clinic at Guy's. His eardrum had burst when mugged soon after arriving in London and I thought it would be a comfort that I spoke Italian.

On the contrary it seemed to make him uneasy and in the end he explained.

"It is embarrassing for me to make this request," he said, "but in these grave circumstances, when my hearing is at stake, I must insist on seeing the professor. I am, of course, prepared to pay."

"I am the professor here," I said. "This is my department!" He remained dubious, as he did not believe me or the nurse and the registrar who assured him that I was indeed the chief.

He made his own enquiries in Italy and returned to see me. This time he was full of thanks and apologies as the specialists he had got in touch with had been amazed that I had seen him myself. He explained that in Italy no one could see the professor unless he was *ricomendato*. Presumably this meant recommended by someone and certainly not just sent up through the Emergency Room.

Anyone appeared to be entitled to recommend. The professor would stop for a moment to buy his newspaper and the vendor might mention his cousin who had an appointment that afternoon and the professor would nod benignly.

It was a matter of exchanging favours, even very minor ones. We can criticise but it is a society based on goodwill, even though it is neither fair nor efficient.

Participants at conferences held in Italy, unless they are used to it, get very edgy as everything promises to go wrong. Speakers never seem to arrive on time, the organisers cannot be found and the whole affair suggests some catastrophe is about to strike. All turns out well instead, good humour reigns and everyone makes a promise to themselves never to take such things too seriously again, relaxes and has a good time.

I had had Italian visitors from time to time and, not long before I retired, it was Calogero Sortino's last day at Guy's. He had brought me a farewell present by way of thanks.

Elaborately wrapped and bound with a blue ribbon, he undid the knot for me, picking at it with the patience and precision that would, one day, make a reliable surgeon and with which he must have tied it in the first place.

He hummed as he did so, or rather recited in an elegant, if outmoded, Italian for his gift had been the poems of Lucio Piccolo, a fellow child of Palermo.

"*…se l'attimo e sgomento*
l'eterno e terrore."

Having finally undone the knot he found the place for me in the book.

"*…if the fleeting is dismay,*" he translated, "*eternity is terror.* You see how he concludes abruptly after a crescendo?"

Calogero was the last of numerous doctors who came to me from many countries. Admirable people who have added a wonderful dimension to my life, some stayed briefly but most were with me for a year, assiduously attending clinics and the operating theatre, and they created the international atmosphere in which I felt at home and thrived. They made my department more colourful than it might have been.

Calogero wanted me to show him one more thing before he left. It was how to tie a bowtie.

*

Most visitors were younger doctors anxious to learn, a few were experienced and may have come only to see what was going on elsewhere so when Jim Donaldson, the chairman and professor of ENT in Seattle, one of the most distinguished surgeons in America, announced that he proposed to come for a year I was quite put out. It would have been rude to refuse and I had hoped he would use me mainly as base to enjoy London but I became apprehensive when it was clear that he intended to follow me like a shadow. He came to every clinic, sat by my side every day as I taught the students, spent time with my research group, was waiting for me when I arrived in the operating theatre and even walked me to my car when I went home.

Altogether it was a bizarre experience.

I was also used to assistants who never hesitated to question what I did as well as give me advice, often unsolicited, but the relationship with Jim Donaldson was entirely different as he was at least my equal in skill and experience.

When he left I found that I missed him. I was so used to doing everything in tandem, checking the look on his face as I made any decision that I was not sure how to continue by myself.

Cultural uncertainty sometimes led to misunderstandings as when an Israeli doctor spent time with us and we were joined by an Iranian, tieless and bearded in what had become their style. He made it clear that he was troubled and assuming that he objected to the presence of an Israeli, I began to make it clear that if he did not like it he could lump it, when the Israeli interrupted.

"No, no!" he explained on behalf of the grateful Iranian. "His problem is that he cannot shake hands with the nurse because she is a woman, but he does not want to cause offence. We have the same problem with the orthodox in Bnei Brak."

We arranged that the Iranian would bow instead and our female staff promised not to touch him.

Those trained in some countries seemed occasionally sinister as lives are not always given equal value, and occasionally I had to consider whether to dismiss someone who spoke about a patient as "from the street".

In some places education imposes barriers to the development of ideas. One young surgeon who was preparing for the FRCS examination was confident enough to admit that he had a problem with some of my more innovative operative techniques, as they were not in the books.

I told him to tell the examiners what he had learned from books as well as what he had seen me do. He found that they were so intrigued that he passed with honours. What had astonished him most was that he was urged to give his own opinion rather than voice received ideas. That need not stop him reading the books or quote them.

Universities that wish to compete on a global scale have to bring together scholars who are leaders in their field whatever their background and wherever they can get them from, and admit students on merit rather than on family connections. In order to attract such people they have to offer good facilities and encourage independent, critical and original thought, rather than try to control or repress it. All of this might be so socially disruptive that many feel it is best to leave things be and remain among the second- or third-class institutions, rather than take the risk of aiming for the best.

Even doctors adhere to different value systems. I realised that in many countries family ties were held as more important than other considerations. It was respect for what they took to be family values but relegating merit to second place hardly gives good results.

This is little different from old boys' networks, which together with misogyny, class distinction, xenophobia and racism may still lurk beneath the surface of our own society, and when merit becomes only one of many considerations, any system goes downhill.

Family networks are often referred to condescendingly as 'clans' or 'cultural differences' to understand them better. Patronising them fails those who have to make their way on merit only, and those disfavoured by caste or ethnicity. It does not benefit anyone, as when promotion of the best cannot be guaranteed it is the second-rate that reign.

Late Reflections

The human body is the best picture of the human soul. — Ludwig Wittgenstein

Maybe, in trying to study the human body, I have got as far as one can when searching for the soul and I have been left mystified.

Most of us do not usually have much to do with philosophy and even less with philosophers, though we respect those linked with moral values, especially when antiquity has tested their wisdom. So I was surprised when Wittgenstein, who had died not many years ago, was mentioned at Guy's.

Few had heard of him despite the fact that, as his war service during World War II, he had worked in the pharmacy, and now someone had suggested a blue plaque.

Connection with celebrity, even if obscure, is always tempting so we agreed unanimously, even though his family had replied to our enquiry that Wittgenstein could have wanted few things less than commemoration of his time as a hospital porter. Hunt's House, the building where he had worked, has since been pulled down and I do not know what became of the inscription.

A refugee from Nazism, he had come from Austria where, curiously, he had been to the same school as Hitler, and as he was of almost exactly the same age since he was born only six days after Hitler he is likely to have been in the same class. Such a coincidence may even have been significant. He was also an aeronautical engineer who had invented a propeller, which is possibly why he has been more accessible to scientists. Misuse of language, he believed, made philosophy appear to be nonsense and he came to blows in Cambridge with Karl Popper, a fellow refugee. Bertrand Russell held them apart and I would like to think that the argument was about profound themes such as free will or the relationship between mind and matter, but the dispute may well have been more mundane.

I never met Wittgenstein but I knew Popper, and did not like what I took to be a defensive arrogance, which hinted he was not being given his due. A consequence, possibly, of past humiliations, but his ideas already had wide acceptance, he had become Sir Karl and had had tea with the Queen, so I felt he should have got over it. Research, he said, begins with a hypothesis we must try to disprove by experiment. If it was not verifiable it was of little value.

I tried unsuccessfully to picture my own work in such a way as his approach was so fashionable, and assumed my failure to do so was the result of a surgical rather than a more academic training, but Popper's views still influence grant applications, which fare better when presented in the form of a verifiable hypothesis. I suspect most of us just try to discover what we can about our tiny corner of the natural world and interpret the findings as best we can. For those who fund the experiments and allocate the grants things may be different.

Reviewing early attempts at understanding nature I followed up a Talmudic story where, presumably seeking immediate illumination rather than plodding study, four sages entered a secret garden hoping to grasp totality. The experience was so shocking that one of them, ill prepared, fell dead while another lost his mind and a third, overwhelmed by improbability, became a cynic. Only the fourth achieved enlightenment.

I was impressed by that medieval parable as I took it to mean, in the statistical terms that we trust today, that even in the best of circumstances and limited to the most learned minds, only one in four of us could achieve ultimate insight. This meant that we should not get too worked up if we fail to be the one, and that a broad understanding of what goes on in life without getting too intense may be enough to see us through.

Scientists yearn for truth and for illumination that will clarify everything, so I wondered if those ancient mystics were trying to trigger a flash of inspiration, whether we call it serendipity, luck or revelation. When I tried to discuss this with Ada Rapoport, a professor at University College London who had a knowledge of medieval philosophy, she gave me an odd look and I had to reassure her that my thinking process had not diverged to the bizarre and esoteric from the straightforward outlook expected from surgeons.

Extending our command of nature, the process we now call experimental research, may always have followed two separate paths, one gathering facts with care and thoroughness and the other hoping for inspiration as well. I told her we had to aim for the first while hoping not to disregard the second if, by good fortune, it presented itself.

*

I did meet other philosophers. I came to admire Ernst Gombrich, yet another Austrian refugee from Nazism who was sometimes called a historian, an art historian and occasionally a psychologist, though I always thought of him as a philosopher. His book, *Art and Illusion*, appealed to me because of his rational approach and because what he said was clear. Much of what he wrote had been intended for young people, and I think technical writers would be more accessible if they address themselves to intelligent teenagers.

We spoke of hearing and music when he told me that what had put him off Schoenberg was that he could not tell if something was good or bad in 12-tonal music. He pressed me about the sense of smell and had ideas on how it could be studied, and I regret that we were unable to follow them up together as we were planning.

A friend of Popper, he respected him and suggested I should reconsider my opinion. I did so and though I was never satisfied by Popper' s scientific arguments, I have appreciated his examination of liberalism and an open society. Today I read what he had said about tolerance and intolerance and find it very helpful in facing what is happening, particularly in our universities and in academia as a whole.

Karl Popper was my father's age and although I now regret that I did not take the opportunity of befriending him rather than getting out of his way, I realise that this could not have been possible. When there is a generational difference it is difficult to form a friendship rather than a teacher-disciple link, and if our views do not permit this then it is best to keep one's distance.

A curious thing about Gombrich was that although he knew so much about art there was little that I could see in his home in Hampstead. I remember that when I visit people who know little about art yet manage to fill their houses with it.

I am told that those like me are called empiricists, a polite way of saying that we reason as we go along. In England and America that can be taken as a compliment so I am happy to do so as I have tried to figure out the natural world in the interest of mankind, an activity recommended as far back as the *Book of Genesis*.

*

'Why did this happen to me?' has been the most common question I have had to face.

I don't smoke, I don't drink in excess, I avoid saturated fats, I eat organic food, I belong to a gym and I take vitamins. There is something religious in a litany of sins of commission and sins of omission. They beg forgiveness, promising to lose weight or take more exercise, and seek a cause for their ills. All are offences against entities, such as nature and the environment.

Randomness terrifies those unable to accept fate and need an explanation for their lot. They often demand action to control their situation and if we cannot offer that, the second best is to give it a name. A virus is often reassuring even if we do not know which one, though it can be no comfort to be told it is cancer, as the naming of ills is an indication that we understand them and maybe can decide what to do about them or at any rate we can try.

Some cultures have evolved an unquestioning acceptance of what is in store. Perhaps that is one reason why the Enlightenment and scientific medicine failed to take root there.

Greek myths tell us of struggles between heroic men and gods personifying the forces of nature. Aristotle, however, probed the natural world while the Bible, intensifying intellectual questioning, often highlights a reversal of divine order and although expulsion from Eden is an escape from blind submission, it is labelled as a punishment. Man is defined as superior even to angels since only he can name animals and plants and this knowledge gives him dominion. Hopefully naming bacteria, viruses and the like correctly will give us control there too.

Job expressed my patients' questions. Why me? I have done nothing wrong, why should this happen to me? It has to do with forces beyond human control but Job endures his lot and surmounts it once he knows that there is a reason, even though not what it is.

A bestseller before writing was even invented, Job's story must have struck a chord as we will not accept that sickness need not have a reason. Some explanation has to be offered, even a dubious one.

Infestation by viruses is respectable enough as a reason today, although there is rarely more evidence for such a diagnosis than that of infestation by demons. When I say that an illness was likely to be a virus, the patient often adds "of course", as though they had only been looking for confirmation of what was obvious.

A doctor, a few dozen generations back, might even have looked like me, nodding reassuringly, sure that it was a pretty benign demon who, helped on his way by daily incantations, would be gone in a few days. His patient would have added "of course", just as mine did, before complaining to his friends about the size of the fee for such an obvious piece of information.

*

Ethics has always been part of the equation.

I had expected that I would be taking the Hippocratic Oath, whatever that was, when I qualified as a doctor. In fact people around me have always believed that we were defined by such an Oath and it was disappointing to discover that we were not expected to swear any such ancient affirmation, though I understand that in some countries a symbolic ceremony is held. We were informed, of course, of the laws regarding medical negligence and had a vague notion that the Oath's main principle was to do no harm.

We ignored completely the four principles of ancient Chinese medicine which, when they started attracting Western attention, proved to have a similar content of humanity and compassion and an injunction to avoid harming the patient. Elements that involve equal treatment for everybody, as well as those recognising the "autonomy" of the patient in the sense of their right to decide for themselves on religious or other grounds, have come to the fore recently as a result of social medicine and personal libertarian attitudes to the common good.

In my youth I took part in elaborate discussions on these subjects until I felt that there was no more to be said and I just did the best I could. Looking back I find that throughout my life the principles I have hung on to have been rather simple and mainly subconscious.

Like most of my fellows I have put the preservation of life first, though today the concept of the quality of that life has been given much attention and, like all of us, I have thought about it and put it in the context of the tools that have become available to us. Nevertheless it is the preservation of life that comes first. I have always felt strongly that we must not harm anyone, particularly in research or novel surgical procedures, but I have also believed that to reject innovation itself can be harmful, so we are required to make complex decisions.

I have no new concepts to offer the next generation other than to adhere to age-old notions of preserving life first, avoiding harm and acting with kindness and compassion. Although everyone would feel better if we could be more than that, we are only human and should only be trusted to do our best.

*

It is now a regulatory part of training but our only formal Ethics lecture as medical students in 1951, three years after the start of the National Health Service, was given by Sir Adolph Abrahams, brother of Harold, winner of a historic Olympic Gold, later enshrined in the film *Chariots of Fire.* He had come dressed in the costume favoured at the turn of the century with wing collar, black jacket and pinstriped trousers.

The main concern at the time was that we should not have sex with our patients, and he made it clear that this also applied to women doctors, who were then still very few. The thought of hauling a female doctor for sexual indiscretion before the Council seemed extremely funny to all of us, including the girls in our class.

Some students were anxious about what they should do should they fall in love with a patient, and Sir Adolph suggested transferring the patient to another doctor to be on the safe side, but insisted that true love should not be stifled so everyone was reassured.

Medical Ethics soon began to deal with controversial issues and had a growing impact as decisions ceased to be theoretical, like who should get the intensive care bed when the choice was between a 25-year-old junkie with AIDS and a 63-year-old breadwinner. It demanded discussion rather than the decision of a single doctor, many of whom sometimes refused to take responsibility, sheltering behind a committee.

Beliefs and customs were classed with ethics.

Jehovah's Witnesses, an obscure little sect at first, came to prominence when they banned blood transfusion. In 1961 they decreed that those who accepted blood, even to save their lives, should be shunned by their fellows and excluded from heaven.

Some surgeons refused to treat them unless they gave permission for transfusion in advance, but I did not. I was uneasy with blanket dismissal as many operations rarely involved severe blood loss, and I was interested because this ban was recent, while other religious principles were so ancient that the initial impulse could hardly be deciphered, much less interpreted. I was watching a new religion as it was being invented.

The blood prohibition was the only thing I knew about them and I suspected it was what defined and held them together, otherwise they were just a minor biblical sect among so many. Their prohibition was probably yet another misrepresentation from Genesis, where God's covenant with Noah lets man control all living things with some conditions, as he may eat flesh but not while it still has its lifeblood. Recalling the transition from animality to humanity, Jehovah's Witnesses may somehow have connected it to transfusion.

I felt protective, perhaps because they were so odd, and agreed to operate without consent for transfusion but it was never an issue until I was presented with a little girl who had an intracranial tumour just beneath the front part of the brain.

The neurosurgeons, unable to take a biopsy without blood and overriding the parents' wishes by making her a Ward of Court, felt it was cruel to exclude a possibly dying child from her community and its heaven, so they called me in thinking that I might be able to reach the tumour through the nose with little blood loss, though there was always a chance of haemorrhage.

The parents wanted to know what I would do in that case and I said I would give blood without hesitation.

"What if we sued?" they asked, and I said I was ready to take my chance but I needed their encouragement before undertaking that difficult procedure. They told me to go ahead and I did not make them sign anything.

Jehovah's Witnesses came to me in increasing numbers as they believed that I accepted their eccentric ideas. My name was mentioned in their journal as a sympathetic surgeon, though I never grasped what motivated them or why they went to such lengths to remain apart from the rest of Christianity. I just did not like to see them mocked when they needed help.

We have come some way from ethics designed to protect doctors from the competition, to a position where many are unwilling to take personal responsibility, and I doubt there is any hospital without an ethics committee.

*

I was surprised when an elderly patient's wife rang as it was not a thing she had done before. I had only treated him for a mild recurrent infection of the outer ear, an irritating but not a life-threatening condition.

What she had to say was disconcerting.

Her husband had been admitted to hospital with kidney failure, she said, but there was no specific cause so it was likely to be age-related as he was well over ninety. The doctors had been very kind and told him that he had two options. They could offer dialysis which would keep him alive if he was willing to attend the hospital three times a week indefinitely, as there was no end in sight, or he might consider calling it a day and just go home with his family. They had stressed that renal failure was not an unpleasant way to go when you are in your nineties so they presented it as a reasonable alternative.

After discussing it with his wife he decided to go home. His children, however, were furious and wrote to the hospital executive to demand that he be treated as he was mentally quite rational and they wanted him alive. The hospital's reply was immediate, assuring him of the availability of dialysis the following day if he wished.

To resolve the quandary he had told his wife to call me and ask me what he should do. He did not ask to speak to me directly and just wanted me to tell her.

I had never had a particularly far-reaching conversation with him and had no knowledge of his beliefs or feelings, so I had no idea why he wanted me to tell him what to do but I had no hesitation in giving a reply.

I told his wife that he should do what he wanted and be pleased that he had a choice. If he was uncertain then he should do what his children had requested and stay alive as long as they needed him.

She complained that she would have to drive him there days a week and hang around the hospital to drive him back in heavy traffic. She made it sound like an imposition as no one had considered the burden it would put on her. I suggested she send him by taxi.

He endured for another 18 months and I never found out how the end was handled, but he had been interviewed during that time and an interesting documentary film about his life was made. Then, I suppose, they let him go.

*

The Dean of our medical school at Guy's fell ill and had to come in as an emergency. The House Surgeon asked who was to carry out the initial examination. Was it going to be the Registrar, someone important like the Senior Registrar or indeed possibly even myself? The Dean, for him, loomed large.

I told him that it was his job and that was what he had to do. If we were to avoid anything going wrong we should do everything exactly as we always did, and the Dean was an elderly gent who deserved the same attention that each of our patients got.

"That House Surgeon who admitted me," the Dean told me later, "examined me so thoroughly, it makes me proud to have taught these young people. What is his name?"

When my own turn came as it inevitably does, the doctor asked if he could bring a group of students to teach on my case. No one had examined me so well and I did feel reassured.

Over our half century physical examination has lessened in importance compared to scans, blood tests and endoscopies as these give a great deal more information. Anxiety may be relieved much quicker by an MRI scan than by cognitive psychotherapy. That does not banish underlying psychological issues but it is a start to know we don't have cancer. Blood tests tell us the state of our physiology, immune system and metabolism, and are beginning to reveal the presence of cancer cells. We can even do our own tests for viruses at home.

*

I had ceased to treat cancer patients but I found myself involved with a man whose disease had become widespread.

He had been a former patient and I had been brought in because, plied with steroids and chemotherapy, he had developed a fungal infection of the throat which troubled him more than anything else. I could treat that and make the end a little easier.

Occasionally there were decisions to be made. He was invited to give a keynote speech at an important event on the south coast and everyone at the hospital had said that he was too ill to give a public talk, but he was desperate to go as it meant that he could express his thoughts and deliver his final advice to that gathering. I suspect that was why he rallied.

I said that if he felt up to it and they were prepared to look after him he might as well go and take a nurse with him. There was nothing to lose, but then he called for me urgently.

"What shall I tell them?" he asked in a panic. "I don't know what to say!"

I pointed out that his hosts, a large church body, sought his guidance, certainly not mine, but I sat with him and listened as he put his thoughts together. All went well as he spoke very movingly and I understand his words were greatly valued.

At the memorial service his family introduced me to one of his very old and very deaf relatives.

"It's the doctor," they explained. "He looked after him."

The old man shouted back as deaf people do.

"He could not have been much good if he died!"

Everyone said "shush" and whispered that it was not my fault.

*

I am often asked why I chose to be an ENT surgeon. It is not an unreasonable question, though no one queries engineers' or bankers' motives, which are presumed to be obvious.

The urge to study medicine responds to some teenagers' needs, perhaps encouraged by TV dramas but requires an interest in science and an ability to pass exams. Then it is a matter of choice and opportunity but the job remains helping people. Some may be retiring or introverted, doing valuable work despite avoiding patients to look at specimens or scans. Some feel a need to help only poor people or only rich ones or deprived populations in distant lands, in deserts or jungles. That is another question.

My younger brother had an ear infection as a small child. He had owed his life to Dr Wolkenstein, a Russian refugee who had come with Gala, his nurse, and performed the mastoid operation that bought my brother time but only penicillin could save him if my parents were able to get hold of it, not an easy feat in Egypt in the last years of the war. Whenever I come across the film of *Dr Zhivago* and his nurse, Lara, the romantic theme by Maurice Jarre plays in my mind and I wonder about Gala and Dr Wolkenstein, my imagination unrestricted as I knew little about them except that they went deep-sea fishing in the Red Sea, an outlandish diversion in our circles. Though not married, they lived together but as adults believed most things should be kept from children, I was discouraged from asking questions.

My mother may have covertly steered me towards ear surgery so that I might look after my brother. Withdrawing from the world as she reached old age, she tried to enclose her family round her in a circle of self-sufficiency where my role was to be in charge of the medical care.

We have to be "good with your hands" to be a surgeon, which is where chance and practice comes in, but if we are to provide the best service possible we must specialise. General surgery no longer applies in the form it did and there is no room now for those people of exceptional ability who tackled whatever happened to turn up.

Subtle intellectual elements are usually present among the surgeons and aspects such as musical, literary or artistic needs often manifest themselves, indicating something other than manual dexterity probably should be also present.

ENT involves all the senses except vision, and hearing leads to reflection on the nature of sound and the distinction between noise and music. If we allow the mind to follow such paths, the development of language offers an interest in education, communication, linguistics and semiotics. Patients come to us with loss of smell and taste, particularly now that we are exposed to neuropathic viruses, making us think of aroma, flavour and a world of savour. The particular problems of the singer affects those special people, and when we face cancer we not only have a direct responsibility in carrying out the operations but we share decision making with radiotherapists, oncologists and imaging experts. It is a world of concepts and ideas and innovation.

Life as an ENT surgeon has been fulfilling. What of the future?

A few years ago in Los Angeles I was allowed to question an old man who appeared life-sized on a TV screen. I was invited to ask him about himself and about events that had taken place 50 years earlier and we engaged in what seemed for a while to be a normal interview. At one point I realised that had he been present at the time we were discussing he could not be alive now and that I was talking to the image of a man who had recorded his story in great detail ten years ago. A voice recognition computer program triggered his replies to my questions, presumably responding to keywords.

I was told that plans were afoot to turn these images into life-size holograms so we will be questioning individuals sitting in front of us. It may be to such a hologram that we will describe our symptoms and investigations, consisting of a finger prick blood test and a whole-body scan will be initiated. Patients will be automatically reassured by the hologram or given basic advice and medication. All this can already happen online but I would much prefer to explain my fears verbally to a kindly hologram, old, young, male or female according to what makes each one feel more confident. An infinite amount of computerised data will be available and recommendations based on probability, a sort of digital Occam's Razor, will be made.

If there is some uncertainty the doctor will be there so I do not think that we can be dispensed with. I hope that if, for any reason, someone would like to see us that they will never be turned away.

It may be that we will be obliged to be part of such a technologically different future but we should regard it as a new tool to help us, not to replace us, and that there will always be a doctor available to help people even though there may not be enough of us.

*

Few regrets have emerged when reflecting on the past as I did what I could and I have also enjoyed my life.

At one point I did turn over in my mind whether I should not have avoided administrative positions like the chairmanship, secretaryship or presidency of this committee or that. I always claimed that it was because of my incompetence in managerial matters or lack of interest in the honours that go with them, but I began to wonder whether it had been simply laziness and that I had been unmindful of some of the duties of leading a department.

These doubts came up when I read of an election for one of the Councils in our profession and I said that I might have stood for that and it was John Hibbert, perhaps the most thoughtful surgeon I have met, who replied. He had been my House Surgeon, my Registrar and was now my colleague. People who have been your assistants get to know you well.

"And we would have voted for you," he said kindly, "but you would have got bored, wouldn't you?"

*

When I took off my white coat on my last day at Guy's Hospital I remembered how in my teens, I had been given the French writer and physician André Soubiran's novels *The Men in White*. The film with Jeanne Moreau meant that the white coat was part of the image I had formed of doctors and already when only students, white coats set us apart.

In white operating rooms, wearing white masks, we bent over patients draped in sterile sheets made whiter by the powerful lights. The only colour was that of blood, red stains that varied in tone according to whether it was venous or arterial.

Later it was felt that green was more restful to the eye but I never knew who decided, perhaps psychologists, commercial advantage or even fashion.

Most have stopped wearing white coats altogether, rumour holding that they are more likely to be contaminated than street clothes. It was also assumed that white coats might be too frightening in children's clinics, and in the psychiatric ward we could not tell staff from patients. Maybe they did not want us to.

Perhaps it was an inclination to blur distinctions between doctors and nurses, seniors and juniors as well as between patients and staff, all of us on a par, working together in a common aim of making everyone better. Maybe doctors can now hide behind modest anonymity, escaping too much being expected of them. It may only be fashion and things could change again as they also slap stethoscopes across their shoulders, like in American films, rather than let them hang from the neck as we had done. I was told it was 'cool'.

Style is often what guides us, and animals, as far as I know, have no sense of fashion. Like many singularly human practices it may have an evolutionary drive. The need for change that moves us towards a new concept and the desire for a new handbag may well stem from the same creative source.

On my last day, in the year 2000, at the start of the millennium, when my last clinic ended and I took off my coat the nurse threw it in the rubbish bin, not the laundry where it used to go. The white coat had lasted around a century from when surgeons stopped walking the wards in black frock coats, only rolling up their sleeves to perform an amputation.

Change is inescapable and all things are bound to change yet again so that patients may demand to see clearly which are the doctors. Documentation is already online and people are getting more familiar with *FaceTime*, *iChat* and *Zoom.* The doctor may soon be observing us from the screen.

But, for as long as one can tell, they will need surgeons.

Acknowledgements

I could not have done anything at all without my wife Gill's companionship and constant support, my sister Claudia Roden's encouragement and Shaun Tan Yi Jie who sought me out in the first place and his team who made everything so easy.

About the Author

Dr. Ellis Douek is a British cochlear implant pioneer and Emeritus Consultant ENT Surgeon at Guy's and St Thomas' Hospital. He is a Fellow of the Royal College of Surgeons and Royal Society of Medicine. He founded the Hearing and Language Clinic at Guy's Hospital, and was the UK Representative to the European Commission on Industrial Deafness. He received the Dalby Prize of the Royal Society of Medicine for his research on hearing. He has over 60 years of experience as a surgeon, and has written 3 books and numerous peer-reviewed articles.

Born in Cairo in the 1930s, Dr. Douek left Egypt to finish his studies in Paris and London, during which time the Suez War broke out and the family was forced to leave forever. He eventually became a famous ENT surgeon at Guy's Hospital in London, where he was one of the first to work on developing a cochlear implant (bionic ear) for the totally deaf. He was also the first to monitor the hearing of a baby at birth, and the first to show a prolongation of the latency in multiple sclerosis. He participated in the development of a middle ear device for the restoration of hearing that now bears his name: Douek-MED^{TM}.

Index

Lightning Source UK Ltd.
Milton Keynes UK
UKHW020644030722
405287UK00002B/133